Hugh Robinson

∞

∞

Yarns from the Ards

tall tales and true stories

Best Wishes

Enjoy

Hugh Robinson

BALLYHAY BOOKS

Published by Ballyhay Books,
an imprint of Laurel Cottage Ltd.
Donaghadee, N. Ireland 2005.
Copyrights Reserved.
© Text by Hugh Robinson 2005.
© Drawings by Tom Heyburn 2005.
Printed by Colourbooks Ltd.

ISBN 1 900935 51 1

Contents

1. Introduction   5
2. The Harvest Fair   9
3. Rose   21
4. The Apprentice Joiner   45
5. A Sweet Romance   73
6. Miss Muldoon   83
7. A Visit from Linfield   93
8. The Big Match   105
9. The Carrowdore Henhouse   119
10. The Joys of Motoring   129
11. Witness for the Prosecution   145
12. Voices in the Ether   163
13. Scrape the Beetle   167
14. A Wee Bit of Christmas Crack   185
15. A Mysterious Meeting   197
16. The Christmas Story   207

Introduction

Yarns from the Ards is my fourth book and my third consecutive volume for Ballyhay Books. *In Back Across the Fields of Yesterday,* my first volume for this publisher, I recalled the humour, characters and way of life in the local countryside just after the war and into the late 1950s. The book was extremely well received. Readers empathised with the warm and happy memories of days gone. Requests came in for a second volume in a similar vein. This led to the writing of *The Book of One Thousand Beautiful Things.* Though still nostalgic and humorous in content and based on real life situations, much of the material tended to be of a more fictional nature. Even so, many readers who enjoyed the book claimed to recall and know the characters and events about which I had written! Happily, I received many requests to produce yet another volume.

It is important for a writer to be true to himself and to his audience. I studied the material which had proved successful in my previous books, in almost seventy broadcasts on Walter Love's BBC Radio Ulster *Love Forty* programme and in my storytelling evenings. It was obvious the nostalgic and humorous content of my work were the elements most favoured by my audiences. In particular, I had observed at first hand just how good it was to leave an audience laughing at the end of a storytelling evening. I thought "a wee bit of crack" with local characters in local situations would be very suitable for my new book. And I had a bagful of as yet unpublished and unbroadcast material flitting around in my head just waiting to be set down on paper.

Yarns from the Ards is, if my writing has been successful, largely humorous. Although nearly all the stories are set around the Ards, I am sure the characters and humour will be recognisable right across the land. Some of the pieces are entirely fictional. Some are a blend of fact and fiction and a few really did happen as they are written. I leave it to my readers to decide which is which!

Yarns from the Ards is not without its share of nostalgia, particularly in the opening chapter that recalls memories of the old Harvest Fair and the characters who frequented it over fifty years ago. Nostalgia and humour blend together in the chapter 'The Big Match'. For many years I had wanted to record something of the atmosphere and crack and banter which took place on the terraces when Ards played their football down at the much loved Castlereagh Park. In particular I wanted to write about what happened when Linfield came to town and the stakes were really raised! However, I did not want to write about a game when Ards were on the wrong end of the score line, as they usually were when playing the mighty Blues. To fictionalise the tale and come up with a favourable result would suffer loss of credibility. Fortunately, my renowned memory recalled a certain match that filled all the criteria I needed. 'The Big Match' is an attempt to give a flavour of the humour and passion of an actual game between Ards and Linfield in the Spring of 1958. I may not have recorded every kick of the ball (it was almost fifty years ago – and I have created a composite picture), though I was at the game! However, I am indebted to my good friends and long time Ards supporters Ivor Edgar, Ards F.C. statistician Billy Graham, and *Chronicle* soccer correspondent Jim Palmer for jogging my memory with factual details they supplied and made my task so much easier.

Though not quite falling into the category of nostalgia, one (for me at least) very important chapter recalls a factual and sad event, which took place in Newtownards nearly one hundred years ago. This sombre chapter was extremely difficult to write and involved several weeks of intense research. But it was one that I very much wanted to lay down in *Yarns from the Ards*. The term, "scrape the beetle", has long since passed into Ards folklore. As a child I had often heard from the old folk the terrible story of the man who allegedly beat his young stepson to death in the infamous Flush Hall murder. I learned later "scrape the beetle" referred to the action of the alleged murderer scraping the blood from the murder weapon and was the name given by the folk of the Ards to the supposed perpetrator of the crime. But beyond the bare facts of the crime, which is still talked about in Newtownards to the present day, I had found it well nigh impossible to obtain any factual written information about the dastardly deed carried out on that dark February night so long ago. I set myself the task of discovering and detailing as much as I could of the crime and laying down, within the confines of a single chapter, the story of "scrape the beetle". I have tried to give a fair and neutral account of that terrible event within the limited space available to me. I am very much indebted to the *Newtownards Chronicle,* its editor Mr John Savage, and the archives of the Belfast Central Library for all their kind assistance without which the chapter could never have been written.

I have always been most grateful to those who have helped me along the way in my writing career. In other volumes I have recorded their names and feel it would be repetitive to do so again, though that in no way lessens my appreciation. I must however record thanks to Tom Heyburn for his superb artwork which prefaces each chapter and the encouragement and continued support shown me by all the staff at Ballyhay Books. A special thanks goes to my hard working and very demanding editor Jane Crosbie who ensured I stuck to the task in hand! Walter Love and the BBC have been a tower of support through the years and have already opened the microphone for me to broadcast the stories within this volume.

Finally, I am most grateful to you, my readers, who have so often shared with me many warm and happy memories and a great wee bit of crack of days that are gone. *Yarns from the Ards* is written for you. I sincerely hope you will find much pleasure within its pages. Thank you.

Hugh Robinson

The Harvest Fair

On September twenty-three,
Will you come along with me?
And we'll go and pay a visit to the Square.
Everybody gathers in,
Tall and short and fat and thin,
For to join the fun and see the Harvest Fair.

There could be no finer introduction to this book of *Yarns from the Ards,* and to the Harvest Fair itself, than this first verse of the old "come all ye" the late Mr Robert Morrison composed in honour of the Fair he loved so well. Mr Morrison's words were simple. Written perhaps fifty years ago, maybe more, they are right on the button and are affectionately remembered and sung by the folk of the Ards to this very day.

Everybody does indeed join in the fun of the Fair – tall, short, fat, thin, young, old – it makes no difference. As September grows weary and autumn leaves begin to fall and misty mornings creep mysteriously over the countryside, Conway Square, in the dear old town of Newton, as those born and bred in it have always called Newtownards, is the place to be. To join in all the bustle and noise and fun that is the Harvest Fair.

Some say the Fair isn't as good as it used to be, that it's lost its character and characters. It's true many of the old-timers who traded and bargained and shouted their wares on Fair day are no longer with us. But folk were saying the same thing when, as a small boy, I was brought in to the Fair from the townland of Ballyhay, near Donaghadee, by my granny. That, as we say, wasn't yesterday. So, at which point in time do we begin to take our reference. And could it be that the passing of time has added a warm glow and rose coloured mist to our fond memories? Perhaps the fault lies not with the Fair, but with ourselves. It may be we have lost the childish innocence to be awed by simple things. As we grow older we fall into the deception of imagining times were much better when we were young. But even yet, there are few about the town of Newtownards and its neighbouring townlands who will not be drawn into the Square on Harvest Fair day.

As children, we loved the Fair. What a noisy, colourful, cheery, open yet enclosed mysterious world of excitement and discovery and adventure it was. It was harvest time. Back home in the fields all had been safely gathered in. We'd sung loudly and thankfully at the Harvest Thanksgiving at Shore Street church on Sunday morning. Now all the richness and abundance of the harvest had come to the town, to the Harvest Fair. Rosy red apples and luscious soft pears piled up in pyramids. Dark purple plums with soft sweet centres, but a first bite that set your teeth on edge. So many of them that they tumbled from the rough table-tops to the ground, scattering everywhere, easy pickings for my chum Dinger Bell and I who, as usual, were on a tight financial budget, and for the pigeons who flapped among everybody's feet. Cans of buttermilk and pounds of freshly made country butter bearing the imprint of the Scottish thistle fashioned by the delicate touch of the butter-pat. Homemade jams - blackberry, damson, plum, strawberry, and raspberry. Candy-apples on a stick and candy-floss, spuds by the ton, cabbages, turnips and carrots piled up all over the place, cheeses, and duck and banty eggs. Whatever your desire, it was right here at the Harvest Fair.

"Get yer yella-man here!" bawled the trader who, it seemed, had only this one day in the entire calendar to make a killing and maximise his profits. "Don't be goin' home without yer yella-man. Only three dee a bag!" For whatever reason Dinger and I held back our hard to come by pennies, we usually parted with them at some point in the day for the grubby little bag of yellow-man. The yellow-man is a rock-like substance, made I suppose, from boiled sugar and a little colouring. It was always piled high on the trader's stall in huge roughly hewn blocks. I can't remember weighing-scales being the order of the day as we parted with our sweaty pennies. The stall-holder simply grabbed a claw hammer and knocked off a couple of jagged lumps which he crammed into a little white paper bag and tossed to us before turning away to bawl out his sales pitch all over again.

I thought then, and still do, that yellow-man was over-hyped. But then, it's an old show-biz maxim you don't over-expose your act. If it's available everywhere, all the time, what you have to offer becomes commonplace, ordinary and devalued and your drawing power is soon non-existent. The yellow-man, which is probably easily and cheaply produced, despite the claims from each vendor that his product is made from the "original and secret recipe" (boiled sugar and colouring?), is rarely seen about the Ards from one year to the other. Why isn't it on the market-stalls every Saturday morning? Or in the sweetshops? If you suddenly crave for a lump of yellow-man in the month of February, where do you go to have your cravings satisfied? Why is this very ordinary product held back for its once a year appearance at the Harvest Fair or the Oul' Lamas Fair? It certainly is a superb marketing job. On Harvest Fair day, in old Conway Square, there aren't too many sets of teeth, young or old, natural or otherwise, which don't have a go at grinding or sucking the sharp lumps of coloured rock into oblivion. Sure, we wouldn't be without it.

Nearly sixty years after I first roamed the Fair I still bemoan the fact I didn't have the two pennies necessary to gain admittance into a small tent in the middle of the Square to see the Incredible Two-Headed Calf. How I would have loved to see the Incredible Two-Headed Calf! Did it also have two sets of eyes? Could it see twice as much as an ordinary calf? Did it have two mouths? Two tongues? Would it eat twice as much as a one-headed calf? Not having the required two pennies to discover the answer to my many questions, I never did find out. But through the years I often wondered what became of the two-headed calf. Did it develop into a two-headed cow and did its enterprising owner then charge fourpence instead of tuppence to view it? Or did it eat its master out of house and home and have to be disposed of? It remains for me an unsolved mystery and an ever-abiding memory of the old Harvest Fair.

Did you ever see fish swim in Conway Square? You will, on Harvest Fair day. Goldfish. Big, small, fat, thin, wearily patrolling the few inches of space and less than half a pint of water within the perilously fragile clear plastic bag which separates them from the rest of the Fair and certain death. The fish used to cost thruppence each. Or, if you were useful with a set of darts, in particular with a set of darts that never seemed to go anywhere near the part of the board you so carefully aimed at, you could win one by successfully striking the centre of the ace on three playing cards pinned up on a plywood board. The board was usually so far removed from the thrower of the darts that he could barely see it, never mind the centre of the three aces. I don't recall too many goldfish changing ownership as the result of three lucky strikes.

The goldfish were usually housed in jam-pots, sometimes two or three to a pot. The more affluent swam about with a certain poise and agility, complete with lightning turns and twists and darts in large fish bowls with an Old Father Neptune dwelling at the bottom for company. At half a crown each they cost a small fortune. I never saw too many of them being sold.

Once, I did buy a goldfish. I cradled my precious purchase in the slopping plastic bag all the way to the bus stop at the

Guildhall and out to our wee farm in Ballyhay. When I got off the bus at Grays Road Ends I carried my fish ever so carefully to our farmhouse and on down to the little river at the bottom of what we rather grandly called our "garden". The "garden" was nothing more than an enclosed quarter of an acre of weeds. With trembling fingers I cautiously undid the bit of cord holding the plastic bag closed and let my fish plop into the water lying at the foot of the hawthorn hedge. I smiled with pride and satisfaction as I watched my fish swim round and round in circles. Not for him the restricted boring confinement of a tiny plastic bag or even a goldfish bowl. My fish was a free spirit. I pushed and prodded at him and encouraged him to travel further, north, south, east or west, any direction, in a straight line. But he was happy enough to swim in circles. I suppose he was used to it. For a long time I rested among the rushes and watched my little friend swim his circles. Then, as the sun set behind the wooded hill, and the foghorn began to mourn beyond the Copelands, I slipped away home to supper and bed. I would see my fish again, in the morning.

In the morning, before I tripped off to Ballyvester School, I ran down to see my goldfish. There wasn't much water at the bottom of our garden. But I couldn't find my fish. Desperately I poked about in the reeds and the rushes. Then I saw him. He was lying, belly up, in a little tributary of dirty water. He wasn't swimming his circles. He wasn't swimming at all. I leaned over and pushed him gently with my forefinger, trying to invoke some life into the strangely still body. But the little fish did nothing more than float away silently at my touch. He was dead.

The death of my goldfish was a great sadness for me, and even more so because I had taken great care to do all I could to ensure his quality of life and freedom by removing him from his plastic jail into the freedom of the wild. Now he was dead. And it was my fault.

I've never forgotten the little goldfish I bought at the Harvest Fair. It was a long time before I came to understand what had caused his demise. The river into which I had slipped him so carefully wasn't really a river. It was a sheugh. It contained nothing more than the surplus boggy rainwater that seeped off the fields from time to time. It wasn't running water and didn't contain the precious life-giving oxygen necessary to life. The water was dead. And so was my goldfish.

Most of the old shops that surrounded the Fair in those days of long ago have disappeared. One of the most famous was Charlotte Heron's fish and chip emporium and ice-cream parlour. Ards folk love to reminisce about the days when they repaired to Charlotte's for a big – it was always big – fish supper and a slider of ice cream. The (even then) old-fashioned booths were always filled, and especially on Harvest Fair day and night. The service was rough and ready. It raised an eyebrow if you asked for a knife to accompany the fork slammed down on the greasy glass tabletop that was usually flowing with spilled vinegar. But the etiquette and surroundings were what we were used to. Nothing in Charlotte's fazed us. Not even the sight of Bobby in his long beige coloured shop coat stirring up the fish and chips in the big fryer at the far end of the emporium. Bobby was partial to a Woodbine. The cigarette was never absent from his lips while he fried the chips, burning and glowing without ever being removed, and the extended inch or so of grey ash every now and then flicked, for convenience, into the chips to lend a little something to the flavour. The story is still related of the days during the war when cigarettes were in short supply and strong demand and often impossible to obtain. One citizen of the town – it may have been Wattie Weir – discovered Charlotte kept a packet or two of fags under the counter for her special customers. Upon learning of this deviousness but unfortunately not being favoured to benefit from it, Wattie immediately coined the immortal words, "Fly man, Charlotte Heron!"

Tippings fish shop was situated a few doors down from Charlotte's, close to Nan and Jack Donaldson's little grocery shop. The Ulster Transport Authority office where the big double-decker buses pulled up before their long run down the Ards peninsula was housed at the corner of the Square and High Street. Geordie Nicholl's bicycle shop faced the town hall. So did the police barracks with its multitude of bicycles stacked outside. Everybody who rode into Newton left their bicycle outside the barracks, working on the theory that no thief, no matter how daring, would have the nerve to pinch their trusty steed right from under the nose of the local constabulary. The theory didn't always work out in practice.

The 'small' Cafollas in the Square was another favourite place for fish and chips and great ice cream. They competed quite well against The Premier, the 'big' Cafollas farther up the same side of the Square. The 'big' Cafollas was a swish place to dine, on the ground floor if you were on your own or with your mates or, if you wished to impress your lady-friend of the time and make even more work for the over-run waitress, climb the stairs to the upper level. Of course at Harvest Fair time folks were hard pressed to find a seat or get an order taken upstairs, downstairs, or anywhere else.

Back out at the Fair, you could plaster your face and hair with a huge pink candyfloss or chew contentedly on a lump of salt-stained purple dulse. The late Benny McAuley was always a regular at the Fair, sometimes with his hoop-la stall, sometimes with his 'hobby-horses'. Benny always had a smile on his cheery face. It seemed anyone could win a prize at his hoop-la stall. All you had to do was drop a wooden ring (three for sixpence) over the prize you sought AND over the wooden block it sat upon. I watched many a ring fall over the prize and on to the block. But I never did see a ring drop over the prize and the block and on to the base of the counter. I'm not suggesting the ring wouldn't fit over the block, but I never saw one that did.

Benny's hobbyhorses, or roundabout, were operated by hand. But the slow-moving rides brought cheery smiles to many a happy youngster. Benny was a character. A real showman. When he passed away he was, as he had previously requested, carried to

Movilla cemetery on a pony and cart without any fuss or grandeur. There'll never be another Benny. But his son Paul can still be seen in the Square on Harvest Fair day and at the Saturday market, thrilling a new generation of pleasure-seekers on the 'hobby-horses'. I stopped for a bit of a yarn with Paul a while back. I commented on the fact he still operated the roundabout by hand, the same as his father had. "Aye," he grinned. "I still have to work at it. Some things never change!"

Gospel preachers preach the Word, the Word that also never changes. In days gone you might have got a song or two from the locally famous street singer William James McAuley. And how often did my chum, Dinger Bell, and the rest of us youngsters, stare goggle-eyed at the writhings of the escape artistes, bound by chains and ropes and locks, head, neck, arms, hands and feet so expertly secured we were quite convinced they'd still be trying to escape when the next Fair Day came around, if ever they lived that long.

Some entertainers could guess your weight, or by sleight of hand adjust their crude weighing machine when you stood upon it to suggest they really had. A gipsy woman would look at your hand and in exchange for silver tell your fortune. I recall Pastor Baird who held the pastorship of the Newtownards Baptist Church relating how he once declined the offer from a Romany by informing her he already knew exactly what life held in store for him. When the gipsy inquired where he had acquired such knowledge the Pastor quoted to her the entire twenty-third psalm. The gipsy did not press the matter further.

Ards man Jules Dorrian remembers the days when farmers from miles away down the peninsula drove their cattle and sheep up the Portaferry Road to the Fair. Jules earned a tanner (two and a half pence) a day for guarding the livestock on the bit of waste ground where the Fire Brigade station now stands. Jules also remembers the gipsies and horse-dealers running their livestock to show off their qualities, up and down the High Street, sparks flying from the iron hooves; the animals frothing at the mouth.

———— ❧ ————

Folk came to the Fair for different reasons. Some came to make a bob or two, some for a bit of crack and some to see if they could pick up a bargain. There always seemed to be plenty of bargains at the Fair. One old character, who traded under the name of Hector, ran a sort of down-market household supplies shop at the top end of South Street. But on Harvest Fair day he locked up the South Street shop and traded from the back of an old lorry slap bang in the middle of the Fair. Hector should have been in show business and I suppose in a way he was. His stage was the back of the lorry. His props were the mountain of products he had to sell, tablecloths, towels, tea sets, breadbins, pictures and dozens of other assorted items he declared he was giving away for next to nothing.

"You'll pay twenty-five quid for it in any shop in this town," bawled Hector as he precariously balanced a six-piece dinner set in one hand and a six-piece tea set in the other. "Worth twenty-five quid of anybody's money! But I'm not askin' you for twenty-five! Not even twenty! Here, niver mind even fifteen." He lowered the swaying piles of china to the floor of the lorry and tossed a cup and saucer to an enthralled lady in the audience. "Take a luk at them missus! Bone china! Luk at the stamp on the bottom. None of yer oul' rubbish there!" He grabbed the cup and saucer back just before the lady could avail herself of the almost opportunity to examine them. He did a bit of juggling with a couple of plates which he declared were of equal quality to the aforementioned cup and saucer. "Here! Forget about fifteen quid! I don't even want ten, nine, eight, nor seven! Forget about six. Who'll give me a fiver a set? At a fiver I'm givin' it away! And here, to make it even sweeter I'll throw ye in a couple of milk jugs. And a butter-dish. At this rate I'm goin' to end up in the poorhouse! I'm givin' the stuff away. I'm givin' it away!"

As a youngster I looked on in amazement as Hector gave away his twenty-five pound dinner sets for a fiver, even though a fiver was an awful lot of money. I wondered at this great generosity of spirit that led to half the town trudging home laden down with tea and dinner sets they didn't need and would probably never use. Hector was a showman. He knew how to sell a product.

Each of us has our own memories of the Fair. The Fat Lady, the two-headed calf, the candy-apples, Benny and his hobbyhorses, gospel preaching, candyfloss, fortune-tellers, hair-restorers, dulse and yellow-man and innumerable other wonders the passing of years have taken away. It may be your memories differ from mine. And maybe you also say, "The Fair isn't as good as it used to be." But I'm sure, if you are at all able, you will, like thousands of others, heed the invitation given by the late Robert Morrison when he wrote:

> *On September twenty-three,*
> *Will you come along with me?*
> *And we'll go and pay a visit to the Square.*
> *Everybody gathers in,*
> *Tall and short and fat and thin,*
> *For to join the fun and see the Harvest Fair.*

> *There'll be William James from Scrabo Hill,*
> *And Hugh from Ballyhay,*
> *Mary Jane from Carrowdore,*
> *And Sam from Drumawhey.*
> *Margaret Ann'll leave the hens,*
> *She doesn't seem to care,*
> *For there's none would take a pension,*
> *For to miss the Harvest Fair.*

> *There'll be piles of yellow man,*
> *And we'll buy some if we can,*
> *For the children nearly eat the stall and all.*
> *Candyfloss stuck on a stick,*
> *Candy apples you can lick,*
> *We'll enjoy ourselves beside the oul' Town Hall.*

You can buy a pound of pears,
Or some second hand chairs,
You can listen to the preacher give the Word.
You can have your fortune told,
By a gipsy brown and old,
You can pay three dee to see a four-legged bird.

If we talk to Farmer Fred,
He will say the Fair is dead,
He will puff his pipe and nod his head and sigh.
But he's talking through his hat,
I'm certain sure of that,
For we'll mind the Fair until the day we die.

Maybe I'll see you at the Fair. Wouldn't it be great if we could meet up and have a bit of crack and banter in the Square and enjoy the fun as we recall those Harvest Fairs of long ago? But in the meantime, I've a bit of work to do, spinning you a story or two from around the Ards. Some of the tales I'm going to tell you actually happened to me. I remember them well, though they happened a long time ago. Others were told to me by my granda and a few were handed down by Rab M'Gilton, a wonderful Newton character who was already old when I was young. So, draw up your chair. Make yourself comfortable. Settle down and we'll enjoy a wee bit of crack and recall days gone while I spin you a few more oul' yarns from around the Ards.

Rose

Nobody ever called her Rose. Not according to my granda who said he remembered the lady very well and told me the story as we sat up late one night waiting for an oul' sow to pig. She was known to one and all as Donaghadee's Maureen O'Hara. But she was ten pounds heavier and a good ten years older than the beautiful colleen who made such an impact in *The Quiet Man* when it had been screened at the Regal a year or two earlier. Even so, she was a looker. There could be no denying it. She was a looker. Admittedly, folks in the 'Dee were divided on whether the newcomer's flaming red hair was as natural as the original O'Hara's or whether it came from a bottle. But she bore such a striking likeness to the Hollywood star in looks and posture and soft southern accent she was tagged with the name as soon as she hit town.

The seaside town was a tightly knit community. Everybody knew everybody, as well as every bit of business there was to know about them. They could place each other with a great degree of accuracy in a hereditary line going straight back three and some-times four generations. Dee folk, from generation to generation, tended to be open-eyed and tight-lipped. And the old saying was true. No way could you call yourself a native of Donaghadee unless, at the very least, your grandparents rested in the local cemetery. The churchyard at the top of the rambling High Street was filled with crumbling headstones bearing the same names as the folk who now dwelled in the harbour town.

But nobody in Donaghadee knew anything about this new-comer. That was the problem. They didn't know where she came from; not even if the name she gave them was genuine. Not that the name mattered anyway. Donaghadee's Maureen O'Hara arrived suddenly, without warning, from nowhere. She was first spotted, not that she could have been missed, in Grace Neill's bar one Saturday night in early summer. She sat quite alone in a warm but darkened corner of the centuries old pub. Heads turned, questioning looks were exchanged and there was much mumbling and whispering as the lady pushed open the door and lowered her head to avoid bumping it on the lintel. The lady smiled, a generous smile, revealing ivory teeth behind warm red lips as she made her way to the seat in the corner. The lady casu-ally removed her long tweed coat and green headscarf. She took a long cool look at the assembled gathering and ordered a glass of pink champagne.

All this had a distinctly unsettling effect upon Grace Neill's clientele. There were various reasons for this. For one, it was rare that un-escorted females, and very few who were escorted, ever invaded the inner sanctum of Grace Neill's on a Saturday night, or any other night. This was a man's pub. Their pub. They relaxed here of an evening after their return from the sea or ploughing the fields or milking the cows or whatever their day's labour had been. Now a woman, a woman they'd never set eyes on, waltzed right in, without as much as by your leave, and plonked herself right down. On Charlie Montgomery's seat, and without even inquiring if anybody was sitting in it. There'd be trouble when

Charlie got back from the Copelands, tied up his boat and came in for his pint of the usual. There'd be trouble. Big trouble. Even more unsettling for the Grace Neill regulars was the fact they didn't know how to cope with the sheer beauty and poise of the interloper in their midst. The long red hair tumbling around her shoulders gleamed like burnished copper in the lamplight. The dark eyebrows, high cheekbones, the green eyes that matched her dress, and that faint fragrance of something they'd never encountered in a cow-byre or in a bucket of mackerel was all too much for them. There was much uncomfortable shuffling in chairs, nudging of elbows, digs in the ribs, little half-covered coughs, furtive looks and not a few whispered half sentences as Davy the bar-man turned the place upside down in an attempt to come upon a beverage reasonably close to that ordered by the lady in the corner.

It was even more annoying for those patrons who had been unlucky enough to be sitting with their back to the door when the lady made her entrance. They had only caught the merest glimpse of the female as she made her way across the floor. They twisted and turned in their chairs, hoping they might at least catch the woman's reflection in the mirror behind the bar. But all they could see was the top of the red head. Bobby Taggart, instead of calling the bar-man as he usually did when he wanted a drink, actually rose to his feet and shuffled over to the bar, stepping as slowly as was decent, taking a long, long look around the premises as if he'd never been in them before and finally resting his eyes, as if by sheer accident, on the newcomer in the corner. Herbie Cully, whose bladder was renowned throughout the town, if not the entire county, as being able to take on board a full night's imbibing without the need at any time for relief, on this particular evening was documented as having made five excursions to the gents. Each of these journeys, because of the roundabout route he took, happily gave him several full and uninterrupted views of the beauty in the corner.

The lady sipped her champagne quietly, a little half smile, perhaps of amusement, played about her lips as she calmly observed the turmoil going on around her. The drink in her glass wasn't quite what she had ordered. But she'd tasted worse. She was relaxed and comfortable in the famous old hostelry, which was more than could be said for the rest of the customers. Each time her eye caught that of a spirit brave enough to glance over at her the eyes of the beholder were immediately averted, his glass lifted, and the pint of porter, which could reasonably be expected to last him the best part of the evening, downed in one go as a sort of penance for daring to set mortal eyes on such beauty.

There wasn't any trouble when Charlie arrived. But shock registered on his weather-beaten features as he stopped dead in his tracks, right in the doorway. He blinked repeatedly and failed totally to even attempt a response to the bright "Good evening" offered by the lady ensconced in the seat Charlie had occupied every Saturday night for the past twenty-three years. Charlie removed his cap. This was later deemed to have been a nervous reaction on seeing the beauty in his chair, for very few folk had ever laid eyes on Charlie's bald pate. Charlie wiped his duncher across his face and stumbled over to his companions who sympathetically made a space for him at the sanctity of their own table.

The champagne, whichever colour it was, lasted the redhead the best part of an hour by which time news, which travels fast in a small town (and even faster in Donaghadee), had got around that something big was happening in Grace Neill's. Suddenly the pub was filled to overflowing. Dart matches in the Oceanic and The Tivoli were abandoned mid-game. Strollers on the pier gave up strolling and practically ran up to Grace's. Even a handful of declared teetotallers were noted to have crossed the threshold of the High Street pub on that famous night.

Finally the object of all interest and curiosity pushed away her empty glass. She rose to her feet. This immediately caused a great stir and then a hushed silence as every patron in the place waited to see what her next move might be. The redhead pulled on her tweed coat. She tightened the belt around her waist, buckled it securely, turned up her collar, checked her appearance in the Guinness Is Good For You mirror, turned, and smiled sweetly upon the entire gathering.

"Good evening gentlemen. It's been delightful. I'm sorry I didn't introduce myself earlier. My name is Rose. I'm coming to live in Donaghadee. I think I'll enjoy it here. Goodnight!" Rose swept out through the door. A total stunned silence remained behind her.

It mattered not what name the striking newcomer had given to the startled company. From the night she made her first appearance in Grace Neill's, Donaghadee had only one name for the redhead who'd landed in their midst. Maureen O'Hara. This was later shortened to O'Hara. On every lip it was "Is O'Hara in tonight?" or "I saw O'Hara out at the Commons today" or "Did you see O'Hara's new dress?"

But the nickname was not a term of endearment. O'Hara was an outsider, an unknown, an interloper, one who had set the town on its ear and made it feel unsure of itself. The entire town and half the countryside had heard about the woman who'd sipped champagne, pink champagne, in Grace Neill's - right in Charlie Montgomery's chair. Who did she think she was? Where did she come from? What did she want? She'd said she was coming to live in the 'Dee. Why? When? And most importantly, where? At the Imperial? The hotel should be classy enough - even for O'Hara. It was hardly likely she'd lodge with Burns the barber. His house in New Street was already overflowing with Bert Mack and his family and the rest of the Pierrot show, which was just setting up stage on the pier for the summer season. Somebody said they'd seen a van delivering furniture to a house out the Warren Road. Somebody else thought they'd seen O'Hara frying bacon over a brushwood fire in the gipsy encampment out at Logan's Bridge. But nobody could produce hard evidence O'Hara was connected to any of these sightings.

Donaghadee didn't have long to wait for an answer to at least one of their many questions about the newcomer. When the citizens discovered exactly where O'Hara intended to live confusion and dismay reigned once more. The tiny cottage, which at one time may have been whitewashed but for many years had been dirty grey with age and decay, had lain derelict out the Cannyreagh Road for longer than even the most venerable of locals could remember. The humble dwelling place nestled in the brow of a steep whin-bush covered hill at the end of a rough lonen, which branched off the country road. The lonen led nowhere and petered out as soon as it reached the ivy-covered cottage.

Nobody ever took the cottage under their notice. Not even the locals had any idea who owned it. Their fathers and their father's fathers, despite every query, question, and much delving into the dusty leaves of local history and poring over the deeds of lands which they themselves owned round about the cottage failed to provide even the slightest clue as to the rightful owner of the property. More than one farmer whose land adjoined the two or three acres belonging to the cottage would have been very willing to talk money and make the highly fertile land his own, at the same time keeping the place in the hands of local folk. But an owner could never be found. No deeds. No history. Nothing. Gradually the place became accepted for what it was, an unsolvable mystery. With the passing of time the cottage and the lonen, which led to it, were all but forgotten.

Until O'Hara hit town. Then everything was turned upside down. The next day, a Sunday to boot, right after O'Hara's memorable appearance in Grace Neill's, a contractor arrived from Bangor with a big mechanical digger to clear the briars and whins and sally bushes that had overgrown the lonely lonen to the cottage. O'Hara was at the head of the work, in a rough coat, Wellington boots and head scarf, pointing, directing and giving instructions, not only organizing but getting stuck in herself, pulling and hauling at bushes and branches and whins and briars, helping to shovel in the load of rough stones on the cleared pathway. She was inside with a yard-brush, scouring down walls and floors, patching up broken windows, and easing rusted hinges with a long spouted red oilcan. She was up on the roof helping to pull the green tarpaulin across it until the broken and missing slates might be replaced. And that very night, for the first time in living memory, the dim glow of yellow lamplight was seen in the lonely cottage at the end of the lonen.

Suddenly evening strolls along Donaghadee's famous pier with the lapping tide and a perfect view of the green Copelands nestling in blue waters were abandoned by the local townsfolk. Now the most desirable place to stretch ones legs and get a good breath of fresh air was the very road that ran right past O'Hara's wee lonen and the old cottage at the end of it. The traffic up and down the switchback road became so intense Tommy Borza, who always had an eye to business, drove out from Millisle and parked his ice-cream wagon at a slap in the hedge just beyond the Donaghadee town limits. Tommy was a happy and jovial man. He made good ice cream. He was also a good businessman. Believed in taking the product to the business. And the business and the crowds were certainly on the dirt track leading out to O'Hara's. Tommy was also astute enough to catch the business twice on the same night - coming and going.

But the Donaghadee locals were not happy. What gave O'Hara the right to move into the cottage nobody owned? There hadn't even been so much as a FOR SALE sign at the end of the lonen to give any of them a chance to bid for the property. And there she sat every Saturday night, in Grace's, sipping at her single glass of pink champagne, smiling like a Cheshire cat, oblivious to the invisible wall of ice which separated her from everyone else. But she never got Charlie's seat again. Once bitten, twice shy, Charlie deputised every one of the regulars to avail himself of his chair on any occasion when he himself was not present. Indeed, he instructed them to make sure someone DID sit in it, thereby denying the use of it to O'Hara at all times.

The sudden and continued non-availability of the chair made not the slightest difference to O'Hara though it didn't escape her notice the seat was always occupied when she dropped in of a

Saturday evening. There were plenty of other seats. But whichever one she choose, it usually brought a sniff of annoyance or a
shake of the head or a spiteful spit on the tiled floor.

The stand-off continued throughout the summer. O'Hara
toiled away at the cottage up the lonen, whitewashing, painting
and even putting in a bit of a vegetable garden at the back overlooking the plantation on the far horizon. Half a dozen Rhode
Island Reds and an aggressive rooster suddenly took up residence
in the rusted corrugated iron shed, which leaned against the gable
wall. The rooster woke the entire housing estate at the edge of
the town every morning at five o'clock sharp. Two or three goats
rambled about as far as the tether around their neck would allow
them, which was up on top of the pile of turf and on to the coal-
shed roof.

With the passing of time some of the locals began, but only
individually and privately, to entertain a sneaking regard for the
redhead from nobody knew where. The woman was obviously
self-sufficient, not afraid of hard work, and she always paid cash
before delivery for anything she bought in the town. And she
had the cottage and the ground around it just as neat and tidy
as anything about the countryside. She attended the occasional
beetle-drive in the Orange Hall, took four books a week from the
library, and every Saturday night enjoyed her single glass of pink
champagne in her favourite hostelry in High Street. It even got to
the point where the locals, meeting her on the street, or even in
Grace's, would sometimes bid her the time of day. Not verbally,
of course. It was unlikely she would ever be accorded such famili-
arity as that. But sometimes there was a nod of the head and,
if she was really lucky, the sun was shining and no one else was
within earshot, a grunt. But O'Hara was, and destined to remain,
an outsider.

Until, that is, the night of the Battle of Grace Neill's, a battle which is still talked about in the town today. That changed
everything. Forever. Donaghadee wasn't unused to the occasional
bus-run from Belfast stopping in the town, sometimes in the

early afternoon, sometimes in early evening. Most of the day-trippers from the big smoke were harmless enough. A bit rough and ready, kiss-me-quick hats, that sort of thing. Maybe a bit louder than Dee folk were used to. But happy-go-lucky with it. The city slickers usually dandered along the pier, around the lighthouse, then back again to enjoy a slider of ice cream from The Cabin or Davy Nardini's. If there was time, a sail out to the Copelands in the Miss Dorothy or The Brothers or the White Heather was a must. If not, Bracewell's Joyland Amusement Arcade stole away their pennies and thruppeny bits as they played the machines and crashed the dodgems and listened to Frankie Laine, Kay Starr, Guy Mitchell and Jimmy Shand on the Wurlitzer jukebox. They usually ended up with a fish-supper in Ernie Giovannoli's cafe and a bag of dulse from Willie McCaw's Blue Dot confectionary shop. The men might have enjoyed a pint or two before heading home to the city, a good time had by all and no harm done. That's the way it usually was.

This time it was different. The Dockers Day Out excursion bus had departed from the Sand Quay in Belfast's Oxford Street for what was billed as "a comprehensive and fulfilling tour of the pleasures of the beautiful Ards Peninsula." The pleasures, namely the pubs of Newtownards, Greyabbey, Kircubbin, Portaferry, Ballywalter, Ballyhalbert, and Millisle, had been a tremendous success with the day-trippers with only a slight question mark placed against the village of Portavogie. Something would have to be done about Portavogie before next year's excursion. Admittedly the entire village, footpaths, roads and gable walls of the houses were painted in the most delightful of holiday colours, indeed, colours which the Dockers Day Out members would have voted for if they had been asked to offer an opinion on a suitable colour scheme for the village. But despite such aesthetic qualities, Portavogie held the unhappy distinction of being the only pleasure of the Ards peninsula to be without a watering hole. No pub. At first the Dockers thought it was a joke. There must be a pub somewhere.

There wasn't. But this oversight was more than made up for when the puzzled revellers reached Ballywalter. Further along the coast road The First and Last public house, right opposite the Ashley Ballroom in Millisle, scored very high points in the hospitality stakes. Until the atmosphere soured and tempers flared when the day-trippers were asked to vacate the premises after only half an hour's concentrated imbibing on the grounds of rowdyism and drunkenness. The trippers, highly principled as they were, declared they would remain not one minute longer in a place where they weren't wanted. They would take their business to where it would be better appreciated.

So they bowled along the Ballyvester shoreline to avail themselves of the final pleasure the Ards peninsula had to offer. Donaghadee, and an evening visit to the historic Grace Neill's pub where, according to the bus-driver, Daniel Defoe, Franz Liszt, and John Keats had oft times enjoyed a leisurely evening. These names, none of which had ever played for Linfield, meant nothing to the Dockers Day Out. But the dockers and their lady friends, who admitted they were not personally acquainted with Mr Defoe or Mr Liszt or Mr Keats, declared if Grace Neill's was "good enough for them people" they would be obliged to give the pub a try. A proposition was voiced, a vote taken and unanimously carried as the bus swept past the Commons towards Donaghadee's High Street. Owing to the loss of valuable drinking time suffered in the dry village of Portavogie, the original planned dander down the pier and around the lighthouse would be cancelled. The remainder of the evening would be spent enjoying the hospitality of the famed Grace Neill's.

The bus screeched to a halt outside the pub as the big red sun sank magnificently behind the Copelands, its dying glory unfortunately unrecorded by the members of the Dockers Day Out. All was quiet within Grace Neill's. All was noise without. The passengers disgorged from the bus. Hardly one was able to stand without the help of a companion. But they all joined in a rousing, if not musically accurate, rendition of "The Pub With No

Beer", a pointed and barbed reference to the fishy and dry village of Portavogie.

Grace Neill's was already well filled when the door crashed open and the Dockers Day Out, failing to observe the single step down into the bar, fell in a heap on the floor among the shocked locals enjoying their usual quiet evening tipple.

Every group has a leader. That one person, that usually self-appointed person, who makes all the decisions for all of his fellows. The Dockers Day Out was no exception. It had a leader. "Barman!" roared the biggest man in the heap as he dragged himself up from the pile of bodies and shoved his way over to the bar. "Set 'em up!"

Davy blinked from behind the bar at the big man whose perspiration and beer stained, formerly white, shirt strained across his fat chest and threatened to burst open at any moment. The man's bullet head and black hair was clabbered in Brylcreem that had melted and trickled beyond his sideburns and down the sides of his face. Davy glanced at the rest of the rowdy clan who had so unceremoniously invaded the premises. He didn't know what to set up. Or to whom it should be set up.

"Is there no sates in this place!" bawled the big man as he wiped his nose with the back of his hand. The nose was about twice the going size for noses and had an interesting variety of hills and valleys and twists and turns running its entire length. Its colour and texture reminded Davy of an over ripe strawberry. He did not impart this interesting observation to the owner of the nose. Mentally, however, Davy immediately nicknamed the big man "The Nose".

"What sort of dump is this!" roared The Nose. He aimed a hearty kick at Charlie Montgomery's chair. "Move over sunshine! D'ye think we're goin' to stand here all night!"

"That's the style! You tell 'em big fella," chortled a lady of indeterminable age but who obviously believed she bore more than a striking resemblance to Miss Marilyn Monroe, right down to the skin tight black skirt, brass ear-rings (each of which was just a shade smaller than a hoola-hoop), and a grubby white gipsy blouse which was having serious trouble containing what it was supposed to be containing. A half Woodbine dangled from the crimson slash that was the lady's mouth. "Here, here, the dackers is here!" she warbled. "There'll be a hat time - in the old town - Tonight! Data-dat-ta-da-d-DA-DA!"

There could be no refuting the fact the dockers and their ladies were indeed in town, much to the chagrin of the Grace Neill regulars. Charlie did as he was told and shuffled his chair across the remaining space available to him. This was approximately two inches, and immediately brought him into shoulder rubbing contact with O'Hara who sat cool as the proverbial cucumber sipping her pink champagne and observing the mayhem going on around her.

"Barman! What about them drinks?" bawled he of the hilly twisted strawberry nose. The man glared meaningfully at Grace's regulars. "Is there no chairs in this place? There's ladies here! With no sates!"

A number of Grace's regulars who up to this point had been enjoying their favourite tipple and the promise of a pleasant evening, suddenly and with one accord remembered they had an appointment elsewhere and were already extremely late for the keeping of it. They hurriedly vacated their seats and made an anxious and awkward exit. The dockers' feminine friends immediately claimed the seats. Davy dragged in a few more chairs from the back store. Eventually the entire Dockers Day Out was seated somewhere in amongst the pub's many nooks and crannies.

Having successfully seated his followers, The Nose called for a Black Bush for himself and one for his lady friend, she of the skin-tight skirt, hoola-hoops and yellow hair. The remaining locals, who had been corralled into one corner of the bar, sat in sulky silence. They watched The Nose take his first slug of Black Bush. He knocked the drink back in one go then banged the empty glass down. He glared over at them. "Cat got yer tongue!" he roared, much to the amusement of his companions. "Can nobody talk in this here town! Anybody got a tongue in their head? Here we are, come all the way from Belfast to see youse, and youse won't even talk til us! Maybe ye'd like to buy us all a drink! Is that what ye'd like to do? Buy us all a drink?"

With no offer of liquid refreshment forthcoming, nor even the hint of a "good evening, how are you, nice to see you, welcome to Donaghadee" nor anything that came remotely near eye contact, The Nose slammed his fist on the table.

"Well! I've got a tongue in my head! And I'LL buy the drinks! But only if one of you country yokels bate me in a drinkin' competition. Now, what do youse say to that!"

The country yokels said nothing to that. They didn't have a great track record in drinking competitions. They drank, when they did drink, for enjoyment. Not competition. The Nose lashed out with his feet, this time at Herbie Cully's chair. "What about you, oul' han'. Do ye think ye cud bate me? Straight whiskies. First fella to refuse pays for the lot. An' for everybody in the bar." He leaned over and leered his fat face that glistened with rivulets of sweat and melting Brylcreem into Herbie's. "I've been drinkin all day, oul' han'. All day long. An' I'll still bate ye! What do ye say? Will ye take me on?"

Herbie's friends turned their eyes upon their companion in hopeful expectation. Maybe Herbie, the best imbiber among them, the man with the famed kidneys, could shut the big man's mouth, good and proper.

It wasn't to be. Donaghadee folk were hard to rile. They weren't renowned for making instant decisions. And Herbie was a third generation Donaghadee man. Admittedly he was a trifle peeved at having his chair kicked almost from under him. But the only indication he gave of his displeasure was the slight whitening of his knuckles and a pursing of his lips as he tightly gripped the wooden arms of his chair. But Herbie couldn't defend the honour of Grace Neill's - and he knew it. Herbie was a porter man. As much as you could carry to him. All night. But he couldn't handle the whisky. Not the whisky. Not even one. He shook his head dejectedly. "I don't like whisky."

"He doesn't like whisky!" mimicked The Nose for the edification of his fellow day-trippers. "The poor wee man doesn't like whisky!" He waved the back of his hand in the general direction of Herbie's companions. "What about the rest of ye? Is there a man amongst ye that'll take me on? For the honour of Danagadee? And Gracie Neill's!"

Grace Neill's was a hushed silence. The Nose leered right into the face of each Donaghadee man, trying to invoke some sort of response. His companions smirked and giggled and the Monroe almost look-alike cackled like an aged hen. But the folk of the Dee sat tight. They spoke not a word, an attribute bred into them through the ages and therefore a very natural response in a situation like this. Every man squirmed uncomfortably in his seat and wished he had had the sense to be part of the earlier successful break for freedom. To make a move now, even if it proved successful, would be a major loss of face, not only individually, but also for the honour of Grace Neill's and the town as a whole. If only help of some sort, any sort, would come from somewhere. Anywhere. But no help was to be found. Until the quiet dignified voice broke the terrible silence.

"I'll take you on."

The men from the Dee lifted their heads. All eyes turned in the direction of the voice.

"I'll take you on," repeated O'Hara as she sipped quietly at her glass. "And whip you. No problem at all."

The Grace Neill regulars covered their eyes with their hands and shook their heads. The situation was going from bad to worse. The champagne sipper – preferably pink – one glass a week – O'Hara – a woman, wanted to take on the big loud-mouth whose nose, quite apart from its interesting geographical features, gave every indication of being the nose of a hardened spirits drinker. Charlie permitted himself the liberty of laying a calloused hand on O'Hara's arm and muttering almost silently "Shshh!"

His request for shshh went ignored. "Well?" repeated O'Hara. She caressed her lips softly with her champagne glass and looked straight at The Nose. "Do you accept the challenge? Or are you all mouth?"

O'Hara's final question, statement, comment, observation - call it what you will - produced a very audible groan of despair from Grace's regulars and a torrent of vile abuse from those visiting for the evening. The shocked dockers, even more stunned than the Dee men, roared for O'Hara's blood. The ladies of the company, led by the Monroe almost look-alike, screeched for The Nose to drink Molly Malone under the table and on to the floor and then send for a donkey and cart to take her back over the Border where she came from.

"I'm waiting," smiled O'Hara, still staring the big man right in the eye.

The Nose slammed his fist down on the table causing the glasses to shake and beer and whisky to slop to the floor. He sneered at the redhead then spat his words into O'Hara's face. "You! You think you could out-drink me? By yerself?"

O'Hara nodded. "You got it in one. You're not as stupid as you look. First man to quit pays. For everybody."

The Nose ignored the insult. He laughed loudly and shoved his table in close to where O'Hara sat at one end of the settle beside the bemused Grace Neill regulars. The remainder of the Dockers Day Out, smelling blood, piled in and around their leader to watch the action, which promised to be a most entertaining finale to their comprehensive and fulfilling tour of the pleasures of the Ards peninsula, and the final humiliation of the country yokels.

"A sniff of the barman's apron'll be enough for her, big fella," bawled someone while others declared "if it was a boxin' match they wuddn't let it start" and "show Miss Hoity-Toity the way a dacker can drink!" The Monroe almost look-alike weighed in with "if ye change yer mind, big fella, I'll take the brazen hussy on m'self!"

Honour where honour is due. The Grace Neill regulars crawled out from the woodwork. They had never at any time accepted O'Hara as one of their own. Nor did they now. If she was stupid enough to take on this big ignoramus in a boozing competition, she was doing it off her own bat. Whatever happened from now on, it was her own fault. Nobody else's. But despite the fact that O'Hara was on a hiding to nothing in an absolutely lost cause, the men of Grace Neill's felt honour bound to give the redhead whatever support they could muster. They huddled closely around her and cleared their throats and murmured among themselves. They didn't go so far as to actually verbally support their would-be champion. But there was no doubt they were with her in spirit, even if they didn't choose to actually nail their colours to the mast.

O'Hara insisted on downing the first whisky. This, she explained to her opponent and his supporters, was to eliminate any charge of foul play or her losing on a disputed technicality or miscount after she had whipped him. She would always be one drink ahead of her opponent.

O'Hara raised the first glass to her eye. She took a long and considered look at it and the liquid it contained. She winked at The Nose who scowled in return. Then she tossed back the contents as if they were so much lemonade. The Nose blinked and scowled again and the Dee men raised their eyebrows. But they spoke not a word.

The Nose swept up his drink and downed it with such speed the spectators on either side barely saw it happen. He grinned and slammed the glass down. "Fill 'em up!" he snarled at Davy. "Ye won't have long to wait for yer money."

O'Hara picked up her refreshed glass and swallowed the whisky without batting an eyelid. The Nose sniffed, took a longer look at the redhead and knocked back his own drink as his supporters clapped and cheered and pushed in closer.

O'Hara and The Nose knocked back four straight whiskies. None had the slightest effect on either party. The supporters of The Nose applauded and cheered and whistled and congratulated their man as he easily did away with each drink. The men from the Dee looked at each other in astonishment and rising interest as O'Hara calmly emptied her fifth glass after she had applied the faintest touch of psychological pressure on The Nose by instructing Davy not to be mean and fill her glass right up to the top.

The Dockers Day Out quietened. The Nose sniffed. He stared at his own glass. He wiped the beads of sweat and melted Brylcreem from his forehead. Then, with a barely noticeable shake in his hand, he reached for his fifth drink. He glared contemptuously at O'Hara as his fingers closed on the glass. He lifted it to his lips and drank it down easily enough. His supporters cheered and whistled and stamped their feet on the tiled floor. "Attaboy, big fella!" trilled his lady friend as she almost suffocated The Nose in an affectionate embrace. "You show 'em how to do it! Show 'em how a dacker can put it away!" But this time The Nose had taken two attempts to drain his glass.

Grace's regulars weren't slow to notice the big man's hesitation, small though it was. They nudged each other and whispered quiet words of encouragement to O'Hara as Davy filled her glass for the sixth time. "Come on, O'Hara. You can do it. You've got him goin'. You can beat him!"

O'Hara raised her eyebrows. She turned and smiled at her supporters. They had actually spoken. Directly to her. Referred to her by name. Not her real name. They'd slipped up there, or had probably forgotten what her real name was. But they had called her by name. The name she knew the entire town used when they spoke to each other about her. She'd heard it whispered behind her back in the grocers, in the library, and in a dozen other establishments in the town. Now they had addressed her, straight to her face, by the name they themselves had chosen for her. She smiled and winked at the men from the Dee, a very slow and a very broad wink. She lifted her glass and poured the whisky down her throat with no bother at all.

The Dockers Day Out shuffled their feet, muttered under their breath and exchanged anxious looks. The contest shouldn't have gone this far. They glanced at their champion. The rivulets of sweaty Brylcreem ran freely down his fat cheeks and into the corner of his mouth. He licked them away with his parched tongue. A blank glaze formed over his beady eyes. Their man wasn't looking at all good as he struggled to focus on the bar and its patrons, all of whom were spinning round and round like Mickey Marley's roundabout. The whiskies and Guinness he'd already enjoyed in every town and village in the peninsula, with the thankful exception of Portavogie, had suddenly caught up with him. His hand shook violently as he gripped his sixth Black Bush and he breathed in rapid shallow bursts. The colour drained from his face and his piggy eyes bulged like hard boiled eggs and his supporters groaned as he set the glass down and wiped his face and lips with the back of his hand.

Consternation showed on the faces of the Dockers Day Out. "Come on! Come on, big fella! Get it down ye! Ye have her bate," shrieked the Monroe almost look-alike as she wrapped her arms around The Nose and pushed her ample cleavage into his face further restricting the amount of precious oxygen struggling to get to his exhausted lungs. The Nose shoved her away and pulled in a mouthful of air. He cursed and grabbed the glass and emptied it in the general direction of his open mouth. Some of the whisky found its way down his throat. He coughed and spluttered loudly as his face altered from deathly white to beetroot red. Most of the drink splashed over his face and chin and dribbled on to the table.

"Foul!" roared the O'Hara supporters. "Foul! He didn't drink it!" But O'Hara raised a finger and silenced them as the big man's head fell forward and crashed on the table with a sickening thud. A low mournful groan went up from the The Dockers Day Out, accompanied by a heart-rending sob from the Monroe almost look-alike. O'Hara's opponent wasn't unconscious. But he wasn't far from it. O'Hara drank down her seventh glass and pushed the big man's drink over beside his chin which rested on the table.

The Nose lifted his head slowly, possibly revived by the vapour of the spirit sitting right under his proboscis. Wearily, he opened his bloodshot eyes. For a full minute he stared at the whisky. Finally, he spoke. "I want... no more drink! Does – does anybody want – to fight? I worked with wee Rinty when – when – when Rinty was the champ!"

O'Hara laughed. "What were you? The punch bag?"

O'Hara's jest hit The Nose exactly where it hurt him most. His pride. He didn't like it. He lifted his hand and swept his glass from the table. It struck O'Hara on the shoulder and splashed the whisky across her chest. Charlie jumped from his chair. But he was too slow in his mission to defend a lady. O'Hara was out of her seat in a flash. She reached for the big docker. He saw her coming and jumped to his feet. But she grabbed him by the front of his greasy shirt and slammed him up against the wall, totally removing the remaining wind from his sails. Even so, The Nose should have had plenty of time to see the punch coming. Everybody else in the establishment did. But not The Nose. O'Hara closed her fist tightly and drew her arm back to somewhere near the front door. Whatever skills The Nose had allegedly learned from wee Rinty when Monaghan was training for his world title bout were of no use to him whatsoever as O'Hara let fly. Her right hand punch caught the big man right on his bulbous hooter, squashing it all over his face, adding yet another valley to the collection already there and drawing forth a fountain of crimson blood.

"Aaaaaggghhhh! You've killed my Freddy!" shrieked the Monroe almost look-alike coming at O'Hara with fists and feet flying as The Nose hit the floor and peacefully drifted off to dreamland. "You've killed my Freddy!" she screamed as she aimed a stiletto heeled kick at O'Hara at the same time letting go with a roundabout right which would have torn O'Hara's head off had it connected. It didn't. O'Hara grabbed Monroe's kicking foot in mid-air, ducked the roundabout right, and while the look-alike hopped about on one leg, caught her right on the chin with a peach of a left hook. Monroe hit the deck and took no further part in the proceedings as the whole place erupted in an uproar of flying fists, feet, threats, screams and general uproar.

The punch-up ended as quickly as it had begun when Sergeant Mateer burst through the door with the other half of the Donaghadee constabulary, namely Constable Wilson. Order was immediately restored. Davy dragged the bloody Nose into a chair and revived him with a few lumps of ice wrapped in a bar towel which also soaked up and stopped the flow of blood. He applied the same technique with similar success to the Monroe almost look-alike who lay spread-eagled on the floor. The Sergeant demanded silence and the immediate cessation of the accusations and threats of further violence issuing from The Dockers Day Out. Once he had established cause of the ruckus he asked O'Hara if she wished to bring charges of assault against The Nose, namely being struck with malice aforethought by a glass of Black Bush whisky thrown by the aforementioned person. O'Hara sweetly declined the offer. The Nose and the Monroe almost look-alike, being the only other patrons in the fracas to have suffered any real bodily harm, were given the opportunity to prefer charges against O'Hara. The Nose, although taking time to reflect upon the offer, decided a court of law was hardly the place to go on oath and acknowledge he had been out-drunk and out-punched by a female from the back end of nowhere. Monroe declared she had been caught by a lucky punch and could "sort yer wumman out any day". But all she wanted to do was get out of this one-horse town and get her Freddy back to civilization where she would make him a big fry and love him after which he would be as right as rain.

Sergeant Mateer sighed and closed his notebook. He addressed himself to The Nose and his beloved as they sobbed on each other's shoulder. "If neither of you wish to prefer charges I'd advise you to get back on that bus before I book you for causin' a breach of the peace, disorderly behaviour, and incitin' a riot. Get outa here!"

The Dockers Day Out huffed and puffed and declared that if

they never came back to Donaghadee it would be a day too soon. The Sergeant turned to Davy as the Dockers Day Out tripped up the step to their bus. "Close up, Davy. I don't want any more trouble here this evenin'."

Davy pointed to the clock behind the bar. "It's only a quarter to ten, Sergeant. Let the boys finish their drinks."

The Sergeant sniffed and shoved his notebook into his pocket. He gazed at the Grace Neill regulars. "Okay. Then close up. The pub's got a good reputation. I don't want to see it ruined." He jerked his thumb over his shoulder as the last of The Dockers Day Out stumbled up the step and into the street. "I don't want any of these eejits comin' back and startin' this all over again."

And so peace returned once more to Grace Neill's on that summer Saturday night. The regulars settled back in their seats to finish up their lately disturbed drink while O'Hara brushed down her dress with the cloth Davy handed her.

Herbie cleared his throat. He laid down his empty glass as O'Hara finished her toiletries. "I say, Rose" he chuckled softly. "Where did ye ever learn to put whisky away like that? You drunk enough of that stuff to fell a pig!"

O'Hara smiled. She dabbed her mouth with a lace handkerchief and checked her appearance in her pocket mirror. She looked around the Grace Neill regulars. "Oh! It's Rose now, is it! And here's me thinking all these months you had forgotten my name, or didn't want to talk to me at all! And now, all of a sudden, it's Rose!" She laughed aloud as Herbie's face coloured and he and the rest of the admonished regulars lowered their eyes. "Ah, don't be worrying about it," laughed O'Hara as she slipped the mirror into her small bag. "It never worried me what you called me. And as for the whisky - sure that was no trouble at all. I was brought up in County Monaghan. By my grandfather. Wasn't it him that owned the wee cottage I'm livin' in up the Cannyreagh Road. Not that he ever took any interest in it. But anyway, my grandfather had a bit of a still up in the hills. Made the best stuff in the County. He was feedin' it to me since I came off the milk bottle.

To get me to sleep and cure the toothache - that sort of thing. Powerful stuff. Powerful. But it got to be I could put it away with the best of them." She pointed to the window where the Dockers Day Out bus was just drawing away from the kerb. "For sure I wasn't goin' to let that big dope throw his weight around in here. I've seen his type before. I could have matched him drink for drink all night. Not that I bother with it these days. But I like a glass of champagne. Now and then"

"That was some punch you hit him with!" declared Charlie. "It was a dandy! Splattered his nose all over his face!"

O'Hara shook her head. "It wasn't that good. I only meant to blacken his eye. When I was a youngster I had an uncle who did a bit of the boxing – amateur style. I used to watch him. Sometimes he'd pretend to spar with me. Y'know, showin' me the moves. How to punch, how not to get hit. He always said it was worth knowin' how to look after yourself. I learned a lot from him." She smiled ruefully. "But my timin' was way off tonight. It was just comin' back when I caught blondie with the left hook!"

O'Hara left Grace Neill's after bidding a fond farewell to her new found friends. Despite the whisky she'd consumed she walked down Hunters Lane and on out the Cannyreagh Road as steady on her pins as any teetotaller. She carried with her the biggest bottle of champagne the pub's regulars, clubbing together, could afford to buy her. From that night on Rose was one of the boys. But she was very conscious of the fact her new buddies were not at all comfortable addressing her as Rose. O'Hara was the name they had always used for her. "O'Hara'll do me, boys," laughed the vivacious redhead. "Just call me O'Hara. The way you always did!"

And they did. On a Saturday night in the old pub as they bought her glasses of pink champagne or greeted her as she walked along the pier or when she invited them up to the cottage of a winter night for a bit of crack. O'Hara was one of the boys. Accepted and respected by all.

O'Hara, happy as a lark, dwelled in the wee cottage of her

ancestors for a number of years. Then she pulled up stakes, sold the cottage - making sure it went to a local - and departed for New Zealand to have a go at sheep farming. Almost a year passed. Then a post-card arrived at Grace Neill's from some wee town near Wellington. O'Hara had got her sheep. Over four hundred of them. She was happy and doing well and hoped everyone in Grace's and the town were too. And if any of the Dee folk ever found their way to New Zealand, there'd always be somewhere for them to sleep at her place. And maybe someday she'd return to the Dee and visit Grace Neill's and recall old times. The post-card was simply signed "O'Hara".

O'Hara never did get back to Donaghadee. But the post-card remained for years, darkened with age and curled up at the corners on the mirror behind the bar where Davy stuck it after everybody had read it. Then, with the passing of time, a new barmaid arrived. In a fit of new broom sweeps clean, the card disappeared. It was never seen again.

But there are still two or three old-timers knocking about Donaghadee who recall the redhead from County Monaghan. Maybe, if you're lucky, you might still find one of them in Grace Neill's of an evening. If you do, it would be worth your while to set him up a drink or two. Maybe, with a bit more luck, you might hear again, from first hand experience, the great story of the Battle of Grace Neill's. And the part that was played in it, by Donaghadee's very own Maureen O'Hara.

The Apprentice Joiner

I first learned about the sport of kings when I was fifteen years of age. I was no longer a boy. I had given up roaming the Harvest Fair and stealing rides on the ruckshifters around Ballyhay, though it is fair to say that even at that venerable age I did not know which sport these kings particularly favoured. But as I was not on nodding terms with any king, or even a prince, my lack of knowledge on this particular subject did not at all surprise me. But I had an open sort of mind and was always willing to learn something new. So in the passing of time, and not very much passing of it, I learned about these monarchs and their sport though in a roundabout sort of way.

It was at number 165 Albertbridge Road, Belfast, on my first day as an apprentice joiner, that I began to learn there was more to life than the haystacks and cornfields of Ballyhay. I learned also of a very easy method of obtaining loads of L.S.D. which was an abbreviation for pounds shillings and pence, being real money before the decimal point was hoisted upon us and nothing to do with the smoking habit enjoyed by some of our citizens today.

At the tender age of fifteen years I commenced to work for a living. That is forty-eight years ago as the crow flies. I have been toiling ever since, so maybe it was a bad habit to start. But I do not complain. I tried my hand at many methods of coming by some shekels to see if I favoured one of them over all the others. Some of these jobs were okay, which is the best I could say for even the most favourable of them. Some were stinkers. I hated them with a vengeance. But I never quit one position until I had another situation to walk into and when I was young there was no problem finding work.

I have sold bread from a bread cart, about which I could a write a book without writing about anything else. I then became a milkman with further disastrous results which I will not dwell upon here as generally speaking milk has many beneficial uses and is frequently used in most households, though no longer my own.

I've flogged televisions and hi-fis. I've made shirts and mini-skirts in the rag trade. I ran a menswear department in the largest store in all of Belfast city, worked on a chicken farm and never eaten chicken since, brushed floors in a flax mill and toiled for Cyril Lord the carpet king. I've done a stint in a newsagents shop, been involved in quality control and work-studies and packed shelves in a supermarket. I've worked with folk who were as straight as the proverbial dye and with some who were as crooked as a corkscrew. Now I write books. And I sell furniture; fine furniture, for Wardens, the oldest shop in Newtownards. Wardens is the finest employer I have ever worked for and I wonder why I only discovered this delightful establishment toward the end of my working life. It is a pleasure to go whistling down the street of a morning and through the portals of a business which has served the community for over one hundred and twenty years and, with a bit of luck, will do so for another one hundred and twenty, though personally I will not be there to see it.

—— ❦ ——

But I get away from my story of how I first learned about the sport which is greatly favoured by kings and for all I know, and I do not see any reason why not, queens as well. It all started when I quit my employment in the George Walker Spinning Mill where I had been employed for some time. I did not enjoy my work in that place though it was a job for life if you were fortunate enough to live that long amid the dust, steam, noise and water which left you a choking coughing spluttering wreck at the end of each day's labour. Many of the people I worked with there, and they were not in the first flush of youth, had many good things to say about the mill, and informed me they had toiled there all their working life and could not wish for better employment. I too was very grateful to the mill on account of it providing me a legal escape from the schoolroom on the day I celebrated my fifteenth birthday. But there all sentiment ended. Now it was every man for himself and I began to seek ways to escape from bondage once again while I still had the mental and physical capabilities to do so. At fifteen and a half years, I was not getting any younger.

I was in luck. While perusing the situations vacant columns in the *Newtownards Chronicle* and *Newtownards Spectator,* I observed a gentleman who went by the name of W. J. Orr and who was in business at number 6a Albert Street, Bangor, sought a bright fifteen year old to serve his time as an apprentice joiner. It appeared W. J. Orr would deem it a great favour if anyone considering himself the personage to fill the bill would make haste to pay him a visit and have words with him with a view to making the position his own.

I was the correct age and therefore easily fulfilled the first stipulation requested by the advertisement. As regards brightness I did not by any means consider myself a dimwit and certainly classified myself as bright and shining and maybe even more so than anyone else who might appear in the line up for this job. I also noted W. J. Orr was in such haste to employ this bright personage he placed his request in not one but two local periodicals. In view of this I did not delay, remembering the old adage that it was the early bird that caught the worm. Next morning I did not board the number seven Newtownards via Moss Road bus for the dreaded mill but threw my leg over my bicycle and made tracks for 6a Albert Street Bangor where it appeared W. J. Orr would be waiting to give an audience to any interested party who has read his advert. Having sought and taken advice as to the whereabouts of Albert Street and already knowing something of the general direction in which the town of Bangor lay, I discovered it no trouble at all.

Number 6A Albert Street was a tumble down half wood half brick shack smaller than one of the hen-houses on our farm, though not in such respectable condition as the place where our hens lived. I walked into the narrow hallway of this dungeon. I saw nobody and nothing but a brick wall in front of me. It was some moments before I noticed the little sliding panel in the wooden partition beside me that bore the invitation to "Please Knock." I knocked.

Naturally, I expected W. J. Orr to poke his head out and say hello and offer me the job on the spot. I was therefore somewhat taken aback but more than pleasantly surprised when the panel slid open and the best looking female I had seen for some days smiled at me from under dark eyebrows and ruby lips and enquired what she could do for me. I experienced a sudden desire to advise her that for starters she might accompany me to the Tonic cinema that coming Saturday night to see *The Tommy Steele Story,* Tommy Steele being my favourite popular singer of the time. But I lacked the guts and anyway I figured if I clinched this job I was perfectly placed when the time was right to make my approach.

I informed this little sweetie I was seeking one W. J. Orr with a view to filling the position he had lately advertised in the *Newtownards Chronicle* and also for good measure in the *Newtownards Spectator.* She advised me Mr Orr was not there. He was in the yard just around the corner at the back of the

———— ∞ ————

office and the possibilities were good that if I went there I would no doubt make his acquaintance.

I gave this little honey one of my best smiles and took my leave of her. But I did not have the opportunity to visit the yard. As the possible future love of my life smiled sweetly and closed the little panel and I walked out the door of the dungeon I bumped into an immaculately dressed gentleman with white hair and whom I reckoned was probably of the three score and ten vintage. He repeated the line my lady friend behind the sliding panel had previously just thrown me.

"What can I do for you?"

I went through the whole speel again and was somewhat surprised to discover this personage was the elusive W. J. Orr whom I was desperately seeking. There was not the hint of a shaving of wood or a drop of sawdust or even a joiner's apron about him and I commenced to wonder if the whole thing was a hoax. However the man shook my lilywhite and expressed a desire to know why I wanted the job. The answer to this question was not immediately upon my lips and I stalled to give myself time to come up with the response he might be looking for. I could not recall any useful hints as to the answer of this question being included in the advert for the bright fifteen year old in either the *Chronicle* or *Spectator*. So I was at once thrown upon my own devices. The money? Didn't think so. I was dropping dough just to get out of the mill and into this position. Because I hated my present job? Didn't sound right. So I told him I liked working with wood. I thought he might like that. And it was true. I had a hammer and saw and a screwdriver back on the farm and once upon a time I had made a pipe rack for my granda and put a wee pelmet up on the window for my granny.

Good answer. W. J. Orr was impressed. I could see it. Then he asked me where I lived and was less impressed. "Ballyhay?" he repeated after me. "Ballyhay? Where is Ballyhay?"

I was somewhat miffed at W. J. Orr's ignorance as to the whereabouts of my townland. I am very fond of my townland.

"Ballyhay is the second biggest townland in Northern Ireland," I proudly informed my prospective employer whose own brightness dropped a couple of watts in my estimation due to his not knowing where Ballyhay was. "Ballyhay is on the far side of Donaghadee," I further advised him. "About six miles from here."

"About six miles from here," repeated W. J. Orr as I looked around to see if I could trace the source of the echo. "And how do you propose to get here every day from Ballyhay to Bangor?"

I studied W. J. Orr a little more closely and began to wonder if I was wise considering taking up employment, if it was offered, with a person endowed with so little common sense. There was only one way to get from Ballyhay to Bangor. Bicycle. Then I thought again of the dust and dirt of the mill and more especially of the little peach behind the wooden panel and whom I would no doubt make my business to meet many more times if I was employed here. I continued my explanation.

"I will ride here on my bicycle," I told W. J. Orr, saying the words slowly, to make sure the message got through to him. "Just as I did to get here now." This was the truth. How else would I get there? The U.T.A. had not yet seen fit to string a bus route from Ballyhay to Bangor, though it often seemed to me it would be quite a good business venture and be instrumental in obtaining very many greenbacks for the company if they applied themselves to do so. But as yet the U.T.A. had not cottoned on to this prospective goldmine. So I was stuck with the bicycle.

"You will ride here on your bicycle?" repeated the echo, which by now I realised was not an echo but words emanating from the mouth of W. J. Orr himself. "You will ride here on your bicycle?"

I nodded. W. J. Orr looked at me as if I was suffering a mental deficiency and for a moment I was happy I had not yet torn up my weekly bus ticket to the mill nor handed in my notice to that venerable place of employment. Then he grasped my lily-white again and shook it warmly. "The job is yours," he beamed.

"Bright boy! Never seen such enterprise. Never! Will ride his bicycle! My goodness! Meet Mr Linton at the yard at eight o'clock on Monday morning!"

Naturally I was delighted to have made the position my own and wasted no time informing the white coat at the mill I would take my leave of the esteemed establishment on Friday evening and could he please have my cards and whatever shekels were due to me ready for collection on that day.

The following Monday I rode the bicycle to 6a Albert Street Bangor and presented myself at the big black gate just round the corner from the office. I found it securely locked and bolted. Neither was there any sign of Mr Linton, or anybody else. But as it was only seven thirty in the morning and I was not supposed to be there until eight o'clock, I took a short tour of Bangor's scenic town centre to while away the time.

When I returned the gate was open and I saw a long narrow builder's yard, which I reckoned ran the whole way down to High Street. A ramshackle wooden hut stretched the length of the left hand side of the yard. The full length of the other side was a dumping ground for old bricks, rotting window frames, empty paint tins and broken doors. A wreck of a Morris van, whose vintage was such I was unable to date it but thought it may have been new before the start of hostilities between Britain and Germany, sat just inside the gate. I considered there was a possibility the colour of this van once upon a time may have been dark blue, but upon this I would not take an oath owing to the amount of scrapes, dirt and dried cement covering the entire bodywork and even the windscreen.

While I was taking in this interesting vista I heard many voices engaged in hearty conversation coming from within the ramshackle hut. Various other gentlemen, whom I took to be professionally engaged in the building trade due to their attire of cement covered dungarees, hob-nail boots and peak caps and tin lunch boxes under their elbow, passed me by. I was not oblivious of the fact my presence in the gateway caused a fair degree of interest to these gentlemen as they walked by and gave me a silent but thorough once-over. Indeed, one or two were so taken by me they came back out from the hut for another quiet gaze upon my person, which commenced to make me feel a mite uncomfortable. I was considering jumping back on the bicycle and riding over to Newtownards and throwing myself on the mercy of the white coat at the George Walker Spinning Mill when a middle-aged man, in somewhat cleaner dungarees than those of his colleagues and sporting a shock of grey hair, came out and greeted me.

"Are you the new apprentice joiner, son?" he enquired of myself as he removed a pipe of tobacco from his mouth. Naturally I was thrilled someone had actually spoken to me and even more that I have been tagged with the prestigious name of joiner right away, albeit prefaced by the word apprentice. But this was a giant step in the right direction. I abandoned my hasty and petulant thoughts of jumping on the bike and riding over to the mill and informed the man this was indeed the case.

"I'm Bob Linton," the man informed me civilly. "I'm the foreman joiner. Come on in to the workshop. I'll introduce you to the rest of the squad."

Bob led me into the workshop, which turned out to be the ramshackle hut running along the left hand side of the yard. The interior bulged with large racks housing every type of timber imaginable as well as sheets of hardboard and plasterboard and other items useful in the building trade, for which at that present time I did not have a name. The floor was littered with empty paint pots, boxes of nails, tins of bitumen and piles of sawdust and wood shavings. A couple of joiners' benches and a circular saw completed the furniture.

I was once again the subject of deep and silent scrutiny by every member of the squad whom I noticed had made themselves fairly comfortably seated on the benches, upturned buckets or wooden toolboxes. Despite the very high risk of fire, I observed that the place was thick with pipe and tobacco smoke as everyone puffed

------ ⸲ ------

away heartily and it appeared I was the only one not indulging in the pleasures of the weed.

"Right, you crummy lot," barked Bob. "This is the new apprentice joiner. And if any of you get up to any funny tricks with him you'll answer to me!" Bob rattled off the names of my new colleagues and then advised me we would be travelling to Belfast where they were presently renovating a small office on the Albertbridge Road. I did not hear this news with any great degree of delight, as I did not have enough money on my person to pay the bus fare to Belfast. However I consoled myself my bicycle was outside the door and if the worst came to the worst, as it very often happens to do, I could pedal up to the big smoke.

Bob pointed to a squat dark haired man sitting on a bag of cement. "That's Tommy Barclay. Tommy's been with us for years. He lives out your way. At Ballyfotherley." Tommy, who in later days transported me to work in his wee motor car without charging me a penny, is a great friend of mine even to this day. He smiled and lifted a hand and waved in acknowledgement. Bob continued. "That fella sittin' on the toolbox is Ronnie Flemming. He's a joiner. Well, almost. He's nearly out of his time. I'll let you work with him today. You'll keep him right, won't you Ronnie?"

Ronnie, solemn faced and unsmiling, nodded in the affirmative but failed to win any brownie points from me owing to his obvious lack of enthusiasm. I learned later this was because my showing up made me the number one threat to Ronnie's long-term employment prospects with the building company of W. J. Orr. It seemed there was an assembly line in apprentice joiners. You start. You learn. You finish your apprenticeship. Then you are out on the cold street to find employment where you will and a new apprentice starts in your place and the whole thing commences all over again. My appearance brought Ronnie's acquaintance with the cold street ever closer, a consideration Ronnie was very well aware of, but which I in my youthful innocence and sense of good will to all men, and especially my new comrades in the building trade, was not.

"Right, you lazy so and sos!" shouted Bob, or words to that effect. "Are you goin' to hang about here all day! Get out there and get that van loaded before I sack the whole lot of you!"

Despite his poker face Bob retained something of a sense of humour while he issued this ultimatum and I thought I would like Bob. I also sensed the lazy so and sos were well aware Bob had no intention of firing any of them. Safe in this knowledge they advised him what he could do with his so and so van and accompanied this with many other threats to his well-being. Bob grinned as the threats upon his person rolled off him like water of a mallard's back. "Give them a bit of a hand there son," he chuckled to me. "And then get yourself a seat on the van. And don't be afraid to push your way in."

That is when I first learned we would travel to Belfast in the four-wheeled wreck outside and I momentarily considered opting for the relative safety of my bicycle. But I pitched in and gave a hand loading lengths of timber while a pimply youth attempted to load a hundredweight bag of cement on to the van and cursed loudly as it split open and spilled the cement all over the ground. A big heavy man who told me his name was Big Sammy and that he was the plasterer tossed on a couple of boxes of nails and advised me the joiners would be lost if they didn't have other folk, namely plasterers, to look after them. Then the back doors of the van were slammed shut and everybody dived into the vehicle to secure himself a seat.

Apart from Big Sammy and Bob, who I understood would navigate the Morris to the Albertbridge Road, I was the last to board. I discovered the rest of the squad piled into the back of the van and seated not too comfortably upon the floor as if they were readying themselves for a Japanese tea party. I was pleasantly surprised to discover the comfortable passenger seat beside Bob's navigating position remained invitingly empty. For what reason, I could not understand. But the old adage says 'never look a gift horse in the mouth' so I took possession of the seat forthwith.

I was no sooner comfortable in this prime seating position

———— ❧ ————

when I became aware of a certain amount of giggling and chuckling from my unfortunate comrades who had been obliged to partake of a seat on the floor. I paid no attention. This turned out to be a mistake of fairly major proportions on my part as the next thing I knew I was the recipient of a hefty clout around the side of the head. The giggling and chuckling from the back of the van broke into unshackled guffaws of loud coarse laughter and cheers as Big Sammy hauled me out from my very nice seating position and dumped me on to the ground.

"That is my sate," he declared in something of a huff. "Get into the back with the rest of the peasants!"

I apologised to Big Sammy for taking his seat and assured him no personal insult was intended. I opened the back doors of the van and scrambled in with the aid of the outstretched arms of my buddies to join the underprivileged in the cheap seats on the floor. I learned pretty quickly they did not particularly enjoy seeing me get cuffed around the head but were delighted I had upset Big Sammy, no matter how innocently, and even if I did not do it with malice aforethought.

I was quite pleased at being chauffeured to the city of Belfast and especially when I learned that no charge would be made upon me for the journey and not a penny would be deducted from my pay when I got it in two weeks after I completed my "lying" week. I found all this a very different world from the George Walker Spinning Mill. No more wailing factory horn. No more iron gate clanging heavily behind me and locking me up like an inmate in Sing Sing. No more clock card to punch. No more dust. No more steam. No more noise. And the crack was mighty among my new mates in the building business. I was on my way to becoming a tradesman. I was the new apprentice joiner. And although I was not immediately aware of it, within a few short hours I was about to learn something of the sport in which kings appeared to take a great deal of interest, as well enjoying the exciting new pleasures of a wee bet on the gee-gees.

I did not observe much of the countryside as foreman joiner Bob Linton drove our wreck of a builders van on the journey to Belfast. This was mainly due to the fact I was bouncing about in the back of the van which contained not only no rear seats but no rear windows and even if there were windows my position on the floor wouldn't afford me the opportunity of looking through them. However the crack was good though the language my fellow workers in the building trade used was not what is considered appropriate in polite circles but I excused this as I had no reason to believe I was mingling within circles of a polite nature.

Just beyond the fair town of Holywood, Bob's sense of direction took a slight detour for the worse and he turned into the municipal dump on the Belfast Lough side of town instead of heading straight for the big smoke and number 165 Albertbridge Road. From my fellow passengers there came much questioning of the quality of Bob's eyesight and a query or two about his driving skills, or lack of them, and he was offered much conflicting advice on how best to achieve our ultimate destination. Bob promptly offered to let any one of the back seat drivers take the steering-wheel if they thought they could do better, whereupon he was instantly advised as to what he could do with his so and so steering-wheel and I began to think Bob's title of boss-man was of an honorary nature only. However the foreman retained possession of his dignity as well as his steering wheel and eventually landed us at our destination at the junction of the Albertbridge and Mountpottinger Roads.

Bob jumped out to open up the terrace house, which it seemed we would be renovating into some sort of insurance office. Big Sammy exited the passenger seat with no bother at all. That was more than could be said for the rest of us as he hauled open the back doors and we all fell out into the street, affording Big Sammy much amusement. I picked myself up from the ground to discover the Albertbridge Road a very busy place at fifteen minutes past nine on a Monday morning. I noted with interest that the red trolley buses humming up and down the road stopped every two or three yards to let passengers off and on in contrast to the bus stops around Ballyhay which were usually half a mile or so apart and the passengers much more fit and maybe not so lazy.

My fellow tradesmen whistled and sang merrily as they unloaded the van of its boxes of nails and bags of cement and lumps of wood. Big Sammy warbled *Some Enchanted Evening* and I was surprised to see he could carry a tune even though he was unlikely to trouble Enzio Pinza. The pimply youth with hair problems rasped out *It Takes A Worried Man To Sing A Worried Song* in the style of Lonnie Donnegan. The worried man informed me he was a founder member of The Checkers Skiffle Group and if I could lay my hands on a decent washboard and a thimble or even a brush shaft and a bit of string and a tea chest, I would be very welcome to take the stage with them at their next gig in the Scout Hall on Saturday night. I thanked him kindly and told him I would keep his offer in mind.

As my new buddies unloaded the van they had the courtesy to take time to wish a very good morning to many sophisticated young feminine type persons who passed along the thoroughfare on the way to their office desks or similar do not get your hands dirtied jobs. I noted that without exception these young ladies failed to return the morning's greetings and did not even turn their head to acknowledge the gentlemen who offered them. This however in no way dismayed my fellow tradesmen who loudly declared for the benefit of most of East Belfast that these young ladies had unfortunately been born with faces like the back end of a donkey which did not necessarily have a high degree of pedigree, and they personally would not care to be seen, dead or alive, in the company of any one of them if there was an opportunity of avoiding it.

Bob shoved open the door of the small office which was sandwiched between Baxters Butchers and The Cosy Cafe. He pushed his way inside, closely followed by the entire company who clutched boxes of nails, lumps of wood, bags of cement and most importantly and carefully of all, tin lunch boxes.

The smell of dead meat from Baxters Butchers on one side of the office, boiling coffee grains from the Cosy Cafe on the other side, wood shavings, new paint and drying plaster and mahogany from inside, assaulted my proboscis as I sauntered in. I saw that the office, if that was what it was supposed to be, was either in the final stages of repair or the initial stages of demolition. Being new to the building trade I was not at this time qualified to form an accurate opinion one way or the other. A joiner's bench covered with wood shavings stood against the left hand wall. I thought I saw beneath it two or three tool boxes buried under a pile of shavings and sawdust. Assorted lengths of skirting board lay in the centre of the floor and a series of electric wires without light bulbs dangled like black skeletons from the ceiling.

I watched the gang as they removed their coats and donkey jackets and carefully hung them up on the end of brush shafts or over the top of doors, and in the case of the pimply skiffler (who had by this time informed me his name was Alfie but when skiffling on stage he was popularly known as Tex) in a tidy heap on the floor. Then there was a stampede in the general direction of the toolboxes underneath the joiner's bench and in various other places around the room. I marvelled at the eagerness of my companions to engage so speedily in the sweat of their brow and earning of their wages. Then I perceived it was not hammers and saws and screwdrivers and trowels and the like which they produced so suddenly from the aforementioned toolboxes. It was black and battered tin tea-cans such as I recalled were a favoured commodity with the roadmen who cut the grass and hedges along the county roads in Ballyhay and Ballyvester.

Some of these cans, which were now produced, had twisted and shaky wire handles and some did not see the necessity to have handles at all. The owners of these distinguished receptacles formed themselves in a circle around me and I saw pretty sharply,

———— ∞ ————

for I wasn't stupid, that for whatever reason, my comrades were about to engage in a game of Ring-a-Ring-a-Rosie. Here I made a mistake. The owners of the cans, who also clutched smaller tin boxes with Tea marked at one end and Sugar marked at the other, held them out to me.

"The tea!" they chorused as one voice while I looked on in bewilderment. There was a stand-off for a period of perhaps ten seconds but which seemed to me like ten hours during which the tin-can holders and I faced each other and waited to see who would blink first. Ronnie made the first move. He stepped forward.

"It's tea-time. You're the gofer. It's your job to make it." He pointed to another member of the clan "Go with Woodbine. He'll show you how to do it. After that it'll be your job to brew the tea every day."

I have described elsewhere within the pages of another book the art of making tea in a wee black can on a building site. Therefore I will here refrain from detailing the subtle skills required in successfully achieving this feat and repeat only that the brew I made and drank from that vessel was the most delectable I ever raised to my lips in my entire life.

As we ambled out to the back yard with the jumble of cans I informed Woodbine that I was most surprised to learn that it was tea-time so early in the morning, especially as we had just enjoyed a very pleasant drive from Bangor and I would have thought it might be time to perhaps engage in the work of the day. Woodbine instructed me not to be daft as there was plenty of time left for work and if I wanted I could do some of it later, and also that the man who made work made plenty of it.

So we boiled the tea cans on a bit of a fire. When they were ready we carried them back into the work area. Woodbine laid his cans on the floor. Then he cupped his hands to his mouth, raised his face to the ceiling and bawled "Teeeeuuuuuup!" in a voice that could be heard back in the builders yard at 6a Albert Street Bangor. Immediately half a dozen voices howled back from various rooms upstairs and downstairs "Teeeeuuuuuup!" and the owners of the voices appeared like rabbits out of hats to claim their own particular can of tea.

Everyone procured for himself a seat of some description, on the toolboxes or the benches or on an upturned bucket, and in the case of Alfie, also sometimes known as skiffler Tex, on the floor. I joined my skiffler friend on the deck and observed my workmates pull the lid from their tin lunchboxes and make an all out attack upon their contents. I was more than impressed to see every one of my colleagues was engaged in devouring the contents of the morning's new-sheets, chiefly the *Northern Whig, Daily Express* and *Daily Mail*. I was not adverse to the written word. I too had been known to spend many hours of pleasure perusing the scribblings of the great literary scribes and I reckoned I had indeed fallen in among as pleasant a group of like-minded souls as I could ever wish to meet. But as they fell to eating, drinking, and reading, I noticed that my associates read only from the back pages of their newspapers and paid no attention to any of the rest.

I bit a piece from the soda-bread sandwich I had the foresight to bring with me from home in case of hunger. Silence reigned. I sensed it. I felt it. There was eating. There was drinking. There was reading. But no talking. I began to wonder if there was a rule in the building trade that stated eating and conversation does not go together. Then suddenly words were flying about everywhere and everybody pitched in with his tuppence worth.

"Well? What do ye fancy in the first race," enquired Big Sammy to nobody in particular as he looked up from his newspaper. "I think Try Hard looks good."

Alfie snorted and I understood from this he did not rate the chances of Big Sammy's nag in this race very highly. "Try Hard!" exclaimed the Saturday night skiffler. "They'll be tryin' hard with hurricane lamps to find that donkey when the meetin's over. To get it ready for the milk-cart in the mornin'!"

I liked a bit of humour myself and this was good stuff.

———— ∞ ————

Everybody, including me, but with the exception of Big Sammy, fell about and laughed heartily at Alfie's assessment of Try Hard's abilities as a racehorse and I reckoned if Alfie failed to make it in the world of skiffle he could do worse than take his chances on the boards as a stand-up comedian. However Big Sammy, who to date had indicated no particular affection for me since I attempted to usurp his seating position in the van earlier, now displayed no great appreciation of humour, nor of my taste in it. He fixed me with a look, which instantly wiped the smile from my face. He tossed the *Northern Whig* at my feet.

"You seem to know a powerful lot about the gee-gees," said he. "Maybe you would oblige us greenhorns with the name of the winner?" He pointed to the *Northern Whig*. "There ye are. There's the runners. Tell us what you fancy, and maybe we'll all get a laugh at you."

I was interested to learn from Big Sammy's very own lips he was indeed partial to a joke though I sensed he enjoyed it somewhat better if the joke was at somebody else's expense and not his own. As for me, I knew nothing about the gee-gees, apart from when they were ploughing fields in Ballyhay. I picked up the newspaper though I hardly knew where to look for details of this race that consumed everyone's interest. But with the confidence, not to mention ignorance, of youth, I did not let my lack of knowledge faze me. I straightened out the back page and made a great play of studying the newsprint thereon. I knitted my brows together and stroked my chin and let my eyes wander up and down the page.

Silence reigned again. And it wasn't only the talking that stopped. So also did the eating of soda bread and the drinking of the strong sweet brew from the wee black cans. I sensed I was making an impression of sorts upon the gee-gee men. I pondered a few moments more just to lay it on a bit before I made my decision and ended their suspense. I folded the *Northern Whig* neatly and tossed it casually across the floor to Big Sammy.

"Golden Plate. Golden Plate will win it. Easily." Now Golden

Plate sounded as pretty a name as anything else I saw listed in the newspaper. As I understood it, this horse had four legs like all the other ponies, so I reckoned it had as good a chance as anything else in the race. And I was pleased to observe my choice had certainly caused Big Sammy to do a bit of thinking. His big white eyebrows knitted together.

"Golden Plate," spluttered the big plasterer as he snatched up the *Northern Whig* and commenced to run his eyes over the back page. "Golden Plate..... Golden Plate? Where did ye get that from? Are you sure it's in the first race?"

"Golden Plate?" echoed skiffler friend Alfie in disdain. "Must be another cart-horse. I never heard tell of it. Must be Try Hard's brother!"

That was when Big Sammy smacked the racing section of the *Northern Whig* with the back of his hand and broke into a fit of raucous laughter and rolled about the floor in such a state I began to entertain doubts as to his sanity. "Golden Plate!" he guffawed loudly. "Golden Plate! I've found it!"

This was good news for me as I was beginning to be somewhat concerned due to the disappearance so suddenly of the nag on which I had recently placed my reputation as a picker of geegees. Unfortunately bad news often follows good, as it did in this case.

"Golden Plate!" chortled Big Sammy waving the *Northern Whig* aloft. "Golden Plate! Here it is boys! It's not a horse at all! It's the name of the bloomin' race! Haw, haw, haw! That's a good un'. The name of the bloomin' race! Haw, haw, haw!"

Now here I must indicate Big Sammy did not actually use the term 'bloomin' when describing the race. But as I write for a certain section of readership who similar to myself do not personally like the word Big Sammy actually used, I will refrain from setting it down here. But the rest of the group took Big Sammy's lead and fell about in various states of mirth and joviality at my stupidity. I joined them in their moment of fun, though I did not fall on to the floor. Then I picked up the paper from where Big

Sammy had let it fall. I again studied the page and saw Golden Plate was indeed the name of the race and I was surprised to learn this as I thought races did not have names but horses only. But I studied the names of the gee-gees again, more carefully, and picked one half way down the list of possible winners.

"Devon Cottage," I announced with even more confidence than when I tipped Golden Plate. "Devon Cottage will win it."

"Are you goin' to back it?" asked Alfie as he leaned over to catch a glimpse of Devon Cottage's form. Before I could reply Alfie wisely informed the rest of the clan that Devon Cottage had four duck eggs. Upon my desiring to be informed what duck eggs had to do with the racing of horses, it dawned upon the skiffler that I was not at all conversant with the ins and outs of betting on the gee gees. "You don't know much about the sport of kings, do ye?" pressed Alfie, which is the first hint I received in my fifteen and a half years that kings also read the *Northern Whig* and had an interest in the ponies. "Your horse has four noughts at the side of its name. Duck eggs. That means it finished nowhere in its last four races. It's a no-hoper. But the good news is," said Alfie as he saw my face fall, "the good news is, it's twenty to one. If you back it and it wins, you'll make a packet of dough. Are you goin' to back it? If you fancy a horse you should always back it. Put somethin' on it."

When Alfie said put something on the horse I was not sufficiently ignorant to believe he was thinking of a woolly blanket. And coming as I did from a farming background I was not unfamiliar with duck eggs and particularly when they were on a plate in front of me and accompanied with several sizzling rashers of prime bacon and several rounds of fried soda bread. However I still failed to see the connection between this culinary delight and thoroughbred steeds competing at Ascot Park where I had been informed this meeting was taking place. But Alfie wasn't far off the mark. I knew nothing about the gee-gees or gambling of any sort. But I had named a winner for the race. It would hurt my pride as well as affect my social standing within the ranks of my builder buddies if I backed down at this stage of the game and declined to put my hard earned money where my mouth was.

"How much do you put on?" I asked Alfie.

"Whatever you like," he responded. "Do a shillin' each way. If it's in the first three you can't loose. There's a bookies in the back alley. I'll put it on at dinner time when I'm doin' the bets for the other boys."

Shillings were not all that easy to come by. But I had two of them in my pocket with which I intended to visit the Regal cinema in Donaghadee that night to see Mr Bill Haley in *Rock Around the Clock,* a film which I understood had been sending teenagers like myself off their rocker when it played in the picture-houses of London town. I was somewhat reluctant to part with one of my two bobs and possibly, if Devon Cottage did not come home at the proper time, fail to see it again, nor join with Mr Haley and his crazy Comets as they made music at the Regal. But having gone so far as to name a winner for the race I could not back down. I pulled out one of my shillings and with some reluctance offered it to Alfie. "Okay. Do me a shilling each way."

Alfie looked with contempt and suspicion at the shilling in my outstretched hand and I wondered why he made no attempt to take it from my lilywhite. Then he confused me even more as he explained the ins and outs and difficulties of placing a bet on the gee-gees and especially if the bet is an each way gamble.

"You need two shillin's if you're goin' to put a shillin' on each way," he explained.

This was news to me. I looked over at Bob. "That's the way it is," confirmed my foreman whom I took to be an honourable man and not the type to con an apprentice joiner out of his last two bob. "You need two shillin's. Shillin' for a win. Shillin' for a place. You see how it works?"

I did not at all see how it worked. I think it is fair to say I did not have the slightest idea how it worked. However I was among sportsmen whose sport as they had informed me was that par-ticularly favoured by kings. Therefore I did not think I was laying myself open to any hanky panky apart from leaving my two shillings to the mercy of the running abilities of Devon Cottage who up to two minutes ago I had never heard off. I reluctantly dragged the other shilling from my pocket and gave the two coins to Alfie. The skiffler informed me he would give me the docket at dinnertime. I nodded. I had no idea what he was talking about.

The tea break, which apparently was contracted to last ten minutes, had already exceeded twenty-five when lunchboxes were finally closed and newspapers folded and slipped into hip pockets. Bob complained it was already half past ten and the day was almost over when we finally dragged ourselves to our feet and my work mates drifted off to several parts of the building to begin earning their pay.

I was disappointed to find Bob had engaged himself in an intricate piece of bench work and assigned me to the non-smiling Ronnie who in turn set me to the brushing of floors both up and downstairs and anywhere else I could find them. This was not how I originally saw myself when I victoriously applied to W. J. Orr, 6a Albert Street, Bangor, with a view to taking up the position of apprentice joiner. I was a tradesman. I should be hanging doors and making stairs and fitting windows. I sensed floor brushing was just a little beneath my level of expectation. After a little while I brought this suspicion to Ronnie's attention.

"Ronnie," said I, as modestly as I could for I am not normally a rocker of boats when they are sailing in reasonably calm waters. "Is there some joinery work you would like me to do? I was very good at woodwork at school. I know all about it."

I began to wonder if Ronnie had some sort of hearing problem. He didn't even indicate he had tuned in to my request. He picked up a length of skirting board he had just finished planing down to a certain thickness. He ran his eye expertly along the bevel. Running his eye along the bevel, you will understand, is tradesman parlance, and in no way infers Ronnie removed one of his very good eyes and rolled it marble style along the length of timber. It simply means he took a good butchers to ensure the wood had been planed straight and level along its entire length. Anyway, I entertained no doubts whatsoever as to the quality of Ronnie's seeing instruments, only his hearing instruments, and was about to speak to him a little louder when he suddenly turned around.

"Listen, son," he almost sneered at me. "You're not at school now. You don't get plastercine and coloured pencils to play with here. This is work. You don't know the first thing about the buildin' game. It'll take you five years to learn it and even then you'll not know it all because there's always somethin' new to learn. And for the first year you'll do nothin' but what you're doin' now - brushin' floors, makin' tea, and takin' the blame for other people's mistakes. So don't come swannin' in here thinkin' you're a tradesman because they let you make a pencil-case at school. Okay?"

I was more than a little taken aback at Ronnie's tirade and I wondered if there was any way I could skip the first year of apprenticeship and go straight into the second. I decided to push Ronnie a bit further.

"Can I nail that bit of skirting board on for you?"

Ronnie looked at me in exasperation. Then he almost smiled. "Do you know where it goes?"

I pointed across the room. "I've been watching you prepare it. It's goes over there. Beside the staircase." Ronnie nodded and reached me the bit of timber. "It's all ready. Put it on with inch and a half sprigs. Only three, where I've made the pencil marks. No more. And make a good job of it or you'll be brushin' floors 'til you're out of your time!"

Naturally I was very pleased to be entrusted with the extremely important job of fixing this bit of wood to the wall right along the floor. I took the sprigs Ronnie handed me. He informed me it was important to use sprigs, which are wire nails with flat heads, as opposed to nails with round heads, which might possibly split the wood. I was already beginning to learn the trade and

I was, as the advertisements to obtain a body like Charles Atlas, the strongest man in the world stated, thrilled and delighted.

I placed the bit of skirting board along the floor and against the wall. I could see Ronnie knew what he was doing with a lump of wood and was a good tradesman. The board fitted perfectly. The marks lined up exactly with the wooden plugs Ronnie had already hammered into the wall to receive the nails. I picked up the hammer Ronnie had loaned me on account of the fact I was new to the business and as yet had not acquired the tools of the trade. I gently tapped the first sprig into the soft white wood. It went in like a dream. I took immense satisfaction in driving it home with a good clout to finish it off. I blattered home the second sprig. Then the third. What a job! Perfect! I pulled at the skirting board. It was well and truly fixed to the wall and in no danger of coming loose unless subjected to a great deal of physical force which I considered would not be called for until many years of time had passed.

There was only one problem. With the skirting board now fixed securely to the wall I had made myself redundant and a year's brushing floors and making tea stared me once again in the face. I looked across the room. Ronnie was engaged with Bob fitting the large window into the front of the building and taking no notice of me. I tiptoed softly over to the nail box and lifted out a handful of sprigs. They were a bit longer than the nails Ronnie had given me previously. But I did not see any of the inch and a half variety so I reckoned what did it matter. This skirting board definitely needed a few more nails just to make absolutely sure it wouldn't fall off, and even more importantly keep me involved in the duties and responsibilities of a tradesman.

I hammered three more nails into the board. They did not go home anywhere nearly as easily as the first three. Indeed one of them didn't go fully in at all but rather awkwardly bent over. While I gazed at the skirting board and pondered the reason for this nail refusing to go in I saw a very strange thing - in fact a sight I never until that particular moment in time saw before.

Water began to seep from the wall just underneath the piece of skirting board that held the bent nail. Now, back home in the sticks I had seen water come from a pump in the field when we went out to fill a can to make the tea in the morning. I had even seen water sometimes gurgle up from the well in the garden. But I never at any time observed water spout forth from a stone wall. This I could not explain. I watched the puddle at my feet grow larger and larger. Then I decided Ronnie might be interested in this strange phenomena, as perhaps he also had never witnessed such a strange thing in all his years in the building trade. And I was the man who had discovered it.

"Ronnie," I called over to my mentor. "Take a look at this. There's water coming out of this wall."

Ronnie was at my side in a flash, leaving Bob to juggle the ten-foot by four-foot mahogany window frame on his shoulder as best he could. Ronnie looked down at the ever-increasing flood on the floor. He glared at me for which reason I did not understand. "How many nails did you put in that skirtin' board?" he demanded, face as dark as thunder.

"Six," I answered proudly. "It's as steady as a rock!"

"How many did I tell you to put in?" roared Ronnie as he grabbed me by the throat. "Three," I choked, coming up with the correct answer and wondering where all this was leading. My senses were not afforded any more time to dwell upon the arithmetic problems Ronnie had set me. He drew off and applied his fist to the side of my head with sufficient force to enable me to view a wide and varied selection of stars of differing sizes and colours even more spectacular to those I experienced when Big Sammy clouted me in the van earlier on.

"You've hit a water pipe! You stupid wee —!" Here again, for the sake of propriety, I do not record the name Ronnie attached to myself except to say it was less than complimentary. "Bob!" he roared as he splashed through the water in similar fashion to Gene Kelly in *Singin' in the Rain*. "This eejit has hit a water pipe!"

———— ∞ ————

Now there was general uproar as every man in the place ran around with mops and brushes and handfuls of sawdust and buckets of sand and I hoped the floor would open up and swallow me as I tried to understand what a water pipe was doing inside this wall where a water pipe had no business being. But regardless of how the water pipe got inside the wall I saw my career as tradesman joiner going down the Swaneee right there and then on my very first morning.

Bob took control. "Alfie!" he shouted to the skiffler. "There's a plumber's shop at the end of the street. Tell him to turn the water off at the mains and come down here as quick as he can! Sammy! Pull them bags of cement away from that water. Ronnie, get that piece of skirtin' off again." He looked at me and shook his head. "You. Grab a brush and get as much of that water as you can swept out into the street!"

The floor did not oblige. It failed to open up and swallow me and there was no place for me to hide. The water supplying the entire street and, as far as I was concerned, the whole of Belfast, was turned off as an attempt was made to effect repairs to the supply pipe I had lately punctured with a two inch sprig. The Cosy Cafe, which specialised in morning teas and coffees, headed for bankruptcy as there was no supply of water with which to prepare the aforesaid beverages and the sale of Paris Buns plummeted as they were much too dry a morsel to indulge in without some form of liquid refreshment to wash them down.

The skirting board was ripped from the wall after which Bob made an all out attack on the plaster to eventually reveal the punctured pipe. The plumber, as fine a man as ever I met, said this was no big problem and he would soon have the water flowing through the system without it being diverted into this particular room of the office block and all over the floor and the half of Belfast. Soon The Cosy Cafe recommenced providing morning teas and coffees except by this time they were afternoon teas and coffees and all ended well although I was demoted back to brushing the floor which duty I fulfilled quietly and gratefully without even a word of complaint.

Big Sammy advised me that in future when I needed water to make tea I need not inconvenience myself by going out to the tap at the back door. All I needed to do was knock a nail into a wall and there would always be a ready supply at my fingertips. But I was pleasantly surprised when Bob informed me my career as an apprentice joiner did not terminate on day one.

"Well, son," said my foreman as he steered the old van through the Holywood Arches, which everybody told me were there though I could not see them, "how did you enjoy your first day as an apprentice joiner?"

"I liked it very much," I answered. "But I am sorry about the water pipe."

"You'll be sorrier on Friday night when the bill for fixin' it comes out of your wages," cackled Big Sammy.

"Never you mind about the water pipe," laughed Bob. "The man that never made a mistake never made anything. But next time you're told to put three nails in a bit of wood, put three in. Not six. Right?"

"Right," I very quickly agreed as I realised I was indeed only a beginner in the skills of the building trade and had much to learn. But if I had made a mistake about the water pipe I certainly did not when I picked a pony to win the big race. Devon Cottage came romping home at twenty-five to one with the rest of the runners wondering where it had gone to and I was in possession of a small fortune while the rest of my comrades did not pick a winner between them all the day long.

However, in subsequent forays in the sport of kings I failed to repeat my initial success that I scored with Devon Cottage. Most of my winnings bit by bit found their way back to the bookie from whence they came. Very soon I realised my early success was something of a fluke. I retired from picking horses which I believed would be first past the winning post due to the fact that now I seemed only to select donkeys or cart horses on the look out for duck eggs. Nevertheless, it is with great affection I sometimes recall my introduction to the sport of kings. And in particular, my first wee bet on the gee-gees.

A Sweet Romance

It was my mate Dinger Bell who did it. Introduced me to the bright lights of Newtownards and all it had to offer a man of the world like myself who had just turned sixteen. Until Dinger, who lived over the fields from us, came along and sowed the seeds of discontent in my fickle heart, I had been happy enough with dear old Donaghadee. The Pierrots on the pier with Bert Mack and Leila Webster, The Regal picture house and the midnight matinees, the dances in the Orange Hall and music and fun and rides on the dodgems in Joyland Amusement Arcade, fish suppers in Ernie Giovannoli's and sliders of ice cream from The Cabin. Who could ask for anything more? Then Dinger threw a large box of spanners into the works, which was reasonably easy for him to do as he was serving his time as a mechanic in Newton.

"Come on up to Newtownards," he said one spring night as he arrived at our farmhouse on his bicycle. "It's great crack up there on Regent Street on a Saturday night. And the talent's great!"

I wasn't impressed. It was true Newtownards was my home

town. And a great wee town it was too. But I'd got used to Donaghadee Young Farmers Club and a nice wee girl I knew there on a Tuesday night and the delights of the 'Dee on a Saturday. And I was working now; I could afford to sit in Ernie's and enjoy a fish supper if I wanted to. Newtownards talent might be great, but I reckoned the Donaghadee girls could hold their own with anything Newton had to offer. But Dinger wouldn't depart the door until I clabbered a dollop of Brylcreem on my hair and pulled out my bike and consented to come up to Newtownards to observe the action on a Saturday night. That was the start of it. I have to admit I was surprised just how good the crack was in the town, whether you were going to see Ards play at Castlereagh Park, or take in the film of your choice in the Ritz or Regent picture houses.

Being a new boy in town it was my good fortune to always have a young lady on my arm when I headed for the Ritz or the Regent of a Saturday evening. But I usually discovered after these happy unions were dissolved, the young ladies who accompanied me to the flicks really were young. And they all seemed to enjoy the same, and for me somewhat annoying, habit of adding a couple of years to their age to bring them on a par with myself. One or two of these fair damsels, who I must admit I'd have been more than happy to continue escorting to the balconies of the Ritz and the Regent until they were of a respectful age, tired of me and sought faces and pleasures anew. I discovered later I was considered by these sophisticated young females to be something of an ice-lollypop. Being from the sticks and an honourable man, I had no idea what they were talking about. But it didn't sound good. However, the parting of the ways, regardless of who instigated it, was always accomplished in the most friendly, satisfactory and civilized manner and usually by mutual consent with no offence taken on either side, never mind the shedding of tears. But this reputation as the ice-lollypop man began to cause me some concern as, after a while, it seemed to be damaging my prospects in the romantic stakes.

But donkey's years later it is still a source of great embarrassment and guilt to me when I recall how it was myself who terminated one of those long ago romances. Dolores – I'll call her Dolores – though that wasn't her real name – because she really was a nice girl and I couldn't say a bad thing about her, had taken a fancy to me. I was a modest sort of fella, not prone to gazing at myself in the mirror, so I didn't pick up on any of the vibes, which apparently Dolores had been shooting off in my direction for quite some time.

Happily for me, the Newtownards girls, and the fellas too, had developed a sort of bush telegraph system that swung into action when a certain individual's antenna was deemed faulty or not switched on to receive the romantic vibes being transmitted. A third party, usually a mutual friend of the one targeted for romance and the one doing the targeting, would let him or her know they were of more than passing interest to a certain party of the opposite sex. This information was in most cases viewed in a favourable light by the receiver when the message finally got through. It did the ego no harm at all to discover that someone you didn't even know existed had laid eyes upon you and was favourably impressed. A response, hopefully positive, could then be relayed back, and matters proceed from that point. It was a good little system and worked well. For the girl, who couldn't very well walk up to the fella and say, "how about it bud?" it provided an opportunity to test the waters on someone she had her eye on. For the fella – well he didn't have to cold call the girl of his dreams and risk the ego-shattering destruction of a refusal and slide several places down the league table of desirable dates for the femmes of Newtownards town. Pride played an awful big part in those innocent romances. The bush telegraph ensured that whatever the outcome, nobody got hurt.

Anyway, word finally reached me Miss Dolores Davidson had taken quite a shine to me and would be willing to accompany me to any Newtownards picture house of my choice on any night I might care to mention, except Thursday. That was because Thursday was the night she always visited her elderly grandmother and took her a small basin of ice-cream from the big Cafolla's in the Square and, it seemed, her granny could not bear to be without her basin of Cafolla's ice-cream on a Thursday night, the reason why I never did find out, and therefore cannot comment upon. Anyway, not being au fait with Miss Dolores but, naturally somewhat flattered by the interest shown in me by a person I did not even know was alive and well on planet earth, I began to make some enquiries.

It turned out Miss Dolores was genuinely of the same vintage as myself, which was a good start. For some time she had been happily employed behind the sweet counter in Woolworth's, having joined that august organisation when they came to town and wiped out the old Crown Stores where Miss Dolores formerly dispensed Penny Chews and Dolly Mixtures and bags of Liquorice Allsorts.

Naturally, I advised my mate Dinger of the approach. Since I'd abandoned Donaghadee Dinger and I went everywhere together - everywhere being the football match or the Ritz or the Regent on a Saturday night or standing on Regent Street watching the girls pass up and down, which they always did without fail of a Saturday and Sunday evening. Normally we did not head off on romantic liaisons independently of each other. We usually worked in pairs, romancing girls who were close friends or sisters or something like that. Naturally we were both more than ecstatic when the good news was received that Miss Dolores did indeed have a sister. We were less than ecstatic when we learned Miss Dolores's sister was only nine years old. I did a bit of quick adding up. I figured that even if the little sister resorted to the usual trick of the Ards females and tacked on a couple of years to her actual vintage, it was still not good enough and Dinger would run the very real risk of spending some time behind bars. I saw this right away and to his everlasting credit so did Dinger. Good mate Dinger, who had been around the block a few times more than myself, said don't worry about it, go ahead with Miss Dolores.

We decided to case the joint where Miss Dolores dispensed the sweetmeats. I did not pass any message back along the bush telegraph to Miss Dolores, barring the fact that her interest had been noted. It was always good not to over react in those situations. The following Saturday afternoon before Dinger and I went down to see Ards hammer Linfield in what was almost the decider for the Irish League Championship at Castlereagh Park, we decided to take a peek at Miss Dolores.

We were old hands at this game. The object of the exercise would be to enter Miss Dolores's place of employment, staying as far away as possible from the sweet counter, while at the same time trying to achieve some sort of view of the lovelorn female to establish where she figured in the beauty stakes. If she passed the long shot test and didn't stray too far from our basic definition of good looks we could move in for a more critical observation from behind the Lego counter. If she didn't get through the first round we could quit there and then with no loss of reputation suffered by either party.

Miss Dolores was no oil painting. But neither was I Errol Flynn and the girl had gone to the trouble to express an interest. I had no other commitment at the moment nor, as far as I could see due to the reputation I had built up as the ice-lollypop man, in the foreseeable future. We took a closer look from behind the boxes of Lego. Miss Dolores seemed amiable enough. About sixteen – genuine sixteen. Average height. Average shape. Average weight. Average looks. Fair hair in a sort of bubble cut. A cheery smile and seemingly a kind word for everyone. I looked at Dinger for a rating. Dinger shrugged. So I decided to consult with our mutual third party to see if Miss Dolores would be willing to accompany me to see Mr Elvis Presley in *Loving You* at the Ritz on the following Saturday evening after she quit the sweet counter.

Word came back along the grapevine Miss Dolores would be

delighted to accept my invitation. She turned up at the duly appointed time. Although the sun was blazing down and the tar was melting the road outside the Ritz, Miss Dolores was wearing a neat little beige trench coat and carried a red umbrella which she later informed me was called Oscar after the Hollywood Actors Award though she was never able to tell me how the connection between the Hollywood Actors Award and her brolly came about. She was also weighed down with enough Mars Bars, packets of Rollo, Spangles and bars of Cadbury's Fruit and Nut to see us through a dozen romantic evenings in the back balcony of the Ritz, or if she decided to go into the confectionary business on her own account, reopen the Crown Stores with some considerable success. When I impressed upon her she should not have troubled herself with all this as I personally had gone to the expense of purchasing a quarter pound of Creamy Whirls for the occasion she told me it was no trouble at all as she got staff discount on everything. I stared at the chocolate bars and packets of sweets bulging from the bags my lady friend clutched to her average breast and wondered if she had to place a minimum order to qualify for the discount.

Miss Dolores was sporting just a little too much make up, too much lip-stick, and more than enough eau-de-cologne and talcum to anaesthetize the entire eligible male population of the Ards peninsula. But she was affectionate. She was kind. In a few short weeks I realised I was the love of her life. But she was just too much for me. After half a dozen Saturday nights in the back balcony where on each occasion I was obliged to try a sample of every single confectionary product available from Woolworth's sweet counter, put away the chocolate ices she insisted on buying me during the interval and cope with her amorous advances as she all but pinned me to the floor in a romantic hold, I realised I had to get out. Quickly.

But I did not know how to break the knowledge of my intentions kindly to Miss Dolores. For all her idiosyncrasies, she really was a nice person. I did not have the cruel heart to tell her face to face I'd had my fill of dolly-mixtures, brandy-balls, toffee bars and huge slabs of pink and white nougat. And also that she outmatched me in the wrestling bouts in the back balcony and it was no contest. I needed, as they say nowadays, to move on.

I have always been of the opinion there is usually an answer to every problem, if you apply a little bit of grey matter to it. So I applied my mind. In no time at all I hit upon a dilly of an idea to terminate the romance. I was contracted to meet Miss Dolores at the Ritz on Saturday night to see my silver screen hero James Dean in *Giant*. I'd seen Dean's first two pictures, *Rebel without a Cause* and *East of Eden*. Dean could act. And *Giant* was a blockbuster of a picture, running about three hours, the sort of picture you need to concentrate on without having to undo half a ton of noisy sweet wrappers and defend yourself from all out romantic aggression at the same time. Top class it was, with a great supporting cast including lovely Elizabeth Taylor, Rock Hudson and Chill Wills. It was my kind of picture. I wished to enjoy it in peace and quiet without having to put away cartons of confectionary and take on Miss Dolores in a winner take all bout in the back row.

I sounded out Dinger. He was a free agent at present, having been disposed of by some charmer who swore to love him forever and then ditched him for a fella who had acquired a second-hand B.S.A. Bantam motor-bike and told her that when he passed his test he would take her on the pillion to places she had never been before. So Dinger was also looking forward to the screening of *Giant*, as he too was something of a James Dean fan.

"Dinger," I said to my mate at half time during the Ards – Glenavon game at Castlereagh Park on the Saturday I was contracted to take on Miss Dolores. "I cannot take any more of this. If I see another Bounty bar I will drop dead. Miss Dolores will be waiting for me at six o'clock at the Ritz to take her to see *Giant*. It is my intention not to be there. Miss Dolores is in many ways, but not all, a very nice person. Personally I do not wish to hurt her feelings by informing her my thoughts are no longer toward herself. I will not turn up. She will get the message and disappear. We will go in to the Ritz at half past six when the coast is clear. She will be long gone. I will be a free agent again!"

Great plan. And I suppose it worked. Well, partly worked. I achieved my aim. Just. But I was not particularly proud of myself. Not that night. Nor ever after. It was a mean thing to do. All these years later, I still believe *Giant* was the best James Dean picture I ever saw. But I did not enjoy it. Not one bit. My conscience, and what happened just before I sat down in my seat in the stalls of the Ritz, ruined it for me. Such was the demand to see Dean's third, and as it turned out, final flick, there was standing room only inside the Ritz. Film fans who didn't have seats were obliged to stand in the long line against the wall, which stretched from the back stalls right down to the very front of the auditorium.

Everything started off great. Couldn't be better. At six-thirty there was no sign of Miss Dolores outside the Ritz. Dinger and I bought our one and ninepenny tickets – when we weren't enjoying female company in the balcony we were always back stall customers – and started the long stumble in the darkness past the standing patrons to the back of the queue along the wall. I was feeling quite chuffed at the simplicity of my little ploy and how easy it all was. Until I felt the sudden tug on my arm and the loud whisper from out of the darkness. "Hugh!"

It was Miss Dolores, true as amber. Even in the darkness her radar had found me and I saw she was ready for action and weighed down with a bumper selection of every sweetmeat currently available in the confectionary trade and obviously willing to immediately overlook and forgive my non-appearance at the appointed time outside the Ritz.

I am not a hard-hearted person. Honest. I would never deliberately cause pain to anyone if I could possibly help it, by word or by deed. But that night in the Ritz I did a very cruel thing. To this day I am thoroughly ashamed of my action. I turned and looked straight into Miss Dolores's face. Then I pulled my arm away, turned, and without speaking a word, followed Dinger down to the back of queue.

Happily, Miss Dolores did not fade away and die on the spot as a result of my cold-heartedness. She survived and pretty quickly got over any sorrow I may have occasioned her. I saw her a week or two later, loading up with Kit Kats and boxes of Roses as an acquaintance of mine, Tipper Brady, came within her sights. Tipper had a very sweet tooth, particularly partial to McGowan's Toffee Bars and slabs of pink and white nougat. I think maybe I did Miss Dolores a favour when I stood her up at the Ritz. Miss Dolores's new romance was a winner from the kick-off. Many a Saturday night I saw Tipper giving every bit as good as he got from Miss Dolores in the back balcony of the local places of entertainment. I was very happy to see it. It soothed my conscience.

Not a long time passed until I saw Miss Dolores sporting a sparkler on the third finger of her left hand. I was informed by those in the know that this was a very important finger for any lady to be sporting such a dazzler, which made me even more delighted. I congratulated myself with a by now crystal clear conscience that I had played no little part in what turned out to be a very long-lasting and very sweet little romance.

Miss Muldoon

Miss Jemima Muldoon was the best looking girl in town. No question. I'd even gone as far as organising a straw pole with Dinger and the rest of my buddies to justify my own personal opinion that Miss Jemima was streets and avenues ahead of all the other femmes fatales in Newtownards, a town famed for possessing more than its fair share of lookers. Miss Jemima won. Hands down. No contest.

The decision was unanimous. Well, it would have been unanimous, if it hadn't been for the dissenting vote of Smiler McClure, so named for obvious reasons, who voted Miss Jemima into second place, just ahead of Miss Lizzie Lappin, a doll who had no right even to be running in the same competition as Miss Jemima. Miss Lizzie Lappin resided with her elder spinster sister in a wee house at the back of the gas works in Mill Street. Smiler's voting preference and choice of good looking ladies was so outrageous the rest of the gang put down a motion to have his vote declared null and void on the grounds he hadn't cast it according to the rules, i.e. to establish the best looker in town. Personally, I go for the democratic way of doing things and convinced the boys to let Smiler's vote stand, citing the well known fact that love is blind and Smiler's ability to behold the truly beautiful things in life had been irrevocably destroyed due to the fact he had unexplainably fallen for the aforesaid Miss Lappin.

The result of the poll was announced as we sat around our fish suppers in Charlotte Heron's delightful eating establishment in Conway Square late on a warm spring afternoon. It proved, beyond all shadow of doubt, Miss Jemima Muldoon was indeed the most beautiful member of the opposite sex in our town and, as far as I was concerned, any other town. Smiler, even with the votes clearly and overwhelmingly stacked against him, would not alter his position that the very best he could do for Miss Jemima was place her a very close second right behind his true love, the bespectacled Miss Lappin.

Not that I'd say anything hurtful about Miss Lappin. As nice a wee girl as you could have wished to meet, if you left looks out of it. But Miss Jemima was a class act. In a different league. Barely seventeen, she had a will of the wisp figure with delicious and delicate curves in all the right places. Her copper bronze hair gleamed like burnished gold in the summer sun. Sometimes she wore her hair loose, tumbling away down beyond her shoulders like Elizabeth Taylor, sometimes tied up in a ponytail, and sometimes pinned and clipped in a beautiful French pleat, every bit as elegant as Audrey Hepburn. Miss Jemima's high cheekbones, dark eyes and generous warm lips and smooth creamy complexion never needed make-up of any sort. She was the closest thing any of us had ever seen to Elizabeth Taylor walking along Regent Street, and I mean when Elizabeth Taylor was the best looking honey on the silver screen. She was a cutie – not Elizabeth – Miss Jemima, and as far as I could see when I first started to hit the town of Newtownards on a Saturday night, she was never without an escort and, it seemed to me, never the same escort two times in a row.

In my wanderings around our lovely streets and lanes I observed that not only was Miss Muldoon never without an escort when she was out taking the air, it was usually a well-heeled escort on each occasion, not to mention handsome as well. It seems she just picked these fellas like ripe plums from the tree of life and tossed them aside when she'd had her fill of them. Still, bowled over by her very real beauty and charm I decided to throw my hat into the ring and make Miss Jemima an offer on one of the very rare occasions when she seems to be temporarily between romances, or, as they say in the acting game, "resting".

My hat was kicked straight back out of the ring. "Oh, thank you ever so for asking," breathed Miss Jemima, flashing big brown eyes I'd die for and fairly taking my breath away. "Maybe later in the season. I'm seeing Ambrose M'Dowell on Sunday evening and after that I may be stepping out with Rodney Stevenson. Maybe later in the year."

I graciously thanked Miss Jemima for her consideration and indicated I might well call upon her at a more convenient time. And I would. I liked her. Miss Jemima, for all her staggering beauty, was not a vain person. To tell you the truth I do not believe she had any idea of how beautiful she was. But there was no doubt the boys were lining up to be her escort. She was a kind person and I think she considered it her duty to honour each of them with her company at some time or another. But I will never forget the night Miss Jemima over-stepped the mark and became the laughing stock of the entire Newtownards town and not a few of its outlying townlands to boot.

It happened this way. On a certain summer afternoon my mate Dinger and I met up with two other men about town, namely big Eddie Jamison, popularly known as Brickie because of the skill he displayed in laying one red brick on top of another on the building site, and Geoffrey Winters. Geoffrey, as far as I could establish, was a personage of independent means and socially a point or two above the rest of us. Anyway, we were seated in Nancy Cafolla's ice cream emporium in Mary Street. Nancy's was a great place to dine, whether the cuisine of your choice was chips, ice cream or hot lemonade, and Nancy wasn't averse to putting it on the slate if you were entertaining a young lady without having the necessary jingles with which to do it. Nancy also had a jukebox that played all the top-twenty tunes. Number one at the moment was Buddy Holly's *It Doesn't Matter Any More,* which in many respects reminded me of my late and traumatic romance with Miss Dolores.

So, we were sitting around the table enjoying the ice cream and the music and shooting the breeze late in the afternoon. Brickie, who was partial to a bowl of chocolate ice-cream with a generous dash of raspberry flavour tossed in for good measure, was getting stuck into the bumper version of the aforesaid delicacy on the table in front of him. Brickie was a likeable chap but unfortunately appeared to have gone AWOL when the good looks were being handed out. He often found it somewhat hard going in the romance stakes.

Geoffrey on the other hand had an over-abundance of everything Brickie hadn't. Educated at Regent House – where else if you lived up the Belfast Road – cultured, refined, good-looking and apparently with plenty of Daddy's dough to go with it. Naturally this made him a formidable prize for the young femmes of Newtownards to aim for. Brickie and Geoffrey came from different ends of the social scale of things. But that counted for nothing in our little group which every Saturday supported Ards football team, haunted the two picture-houses and occasionally bopped the night away at the Queens Hall. But Nancy's cafe, with its jukebox full of Buddy Holly and Everley Brothers records and superb chocolate ices, was a regular rendezvous for us to while away the time late on a summer Saturday afternoon.

"What are you doing tonight, big fella," I asked Brickie as he continued to demolish his chocolate and raspberry ice cream.

Brickie, whom I observed was more than usually well turned out on this occasion and without a trace of cement or plaster about his person, appeared to sprout another six inches in height as he straightened himself in his chair. "Tonight," he beamed, laying a certain emphasis upon the word 'tonight', "tonight I am taking Miss Jemima Muldoon to the pictures! We will see *Gunfight at the O. K. Corral.* Kirk Douglas is in it. It should be a good show. And Frankie Laine sings the theme song".

I raised an eyebrow. Frankie Laine was no mean singer and *Gunfight at the O.K. Corral* was a peach of a picture and reckoned to be one of the best westerns to hit Newton for some time. Not having on this particular evening any romantic engagements of my own I intended to pay a visit to see it for myself. But I wondered how Brickie had managed to jump several pages ahead of me in Miss Jemima's social calendar. It just went to prove Miss Jemima had no time for favouritism and gave everybody a fair crack of the whip. Brickie rammed another liberal portion of Nancy's chocolate and raspberry ice cream down his throat and licked his lips.

But on hearing Brickie's declaration of intent the immaculate handsome Geoffrey turned quite pale and ceased in the enjoyment of his own ice-cream, the spoon half way between bowl and mouth, causing me to ponder on the old adage there's many a slip twixt cup and lip. As yet I had no way of knowing what the slip in this case was going to be. But I sensed a fairly big clue was about to come along any moment. Geoffrey slowly lowered his spoon, complete with its dollop of ice cream, back into the bowl.

"Edward," said Geoffrey, "am I to understand you are under the impression you have an arrangement to meet with Miss Jemima Muldoon? This evening?"

Brickie scraped his spoon noisily around the bottom of his empty ice-cream bowl and beamed. "With the one and only. At the Regent. Six o'clock. *Gunfight at the O.K. Corral.*"

Geoffrey pushed away his bowl and although I am not normally a suspicious type of person I imagined I detected some little irritation upon his handsome features though he did his best to conceal this. He leaned back in his chair. He stared acutely at Brickie. Now I was certain something had caused Geoffrey some little consternation though as yet I was unable to pin down exactly what this might be. "Edward," murmured Geoffrey, "are we speaking of the same Miss Jemima Muldoon?"

Brickie resorted to licking the back of his spoon which he was obliged to do owing to the absence of ice-cream remaining in the bowl. "I do not know which Miss Jemima Muldoon you are talkin' about, Geoffrey. But I know which one I'm talkin' about. The Miss Jemima Muldoon who is the best lukkin' wumman in this town."

I noted the stunned look on Geoffrey's handsome features. His face changed colour to match that of his ice cream, which was of the vanilla type and not raspberry flavour. He leaned over the table and looked directly at the apprentice bricklayer, addressing him in a dry parched voice, but without, to give Geoffrey his due, enmity of any sort. "Well, Edward. It may be of some interest to you to know that I also have an appointment with Miss Jemima this evening. And also at six o'clock. We are going to the Ritz. To see *Compulsion*. It is a psychological thriller adapted from the best-selling novel by Meyer Levin. When I explained the intrigues of the plot to Miss Jemima and the importance of this film in the history of modern cinema and the critical acclaim it has received in London she advised me she would be nothing less than thrilled to accompany me to the screening this evening. At six o'clock."

Well! Here was a turn up for the proverbial books. It appeared Miss Jemima, in an attempt to speedily fulfil the outstanding commitments in her diary and clear the way for the new season, had double booked. She double booked not only on the same night, but also at the same time, though fortunately not at the same venue. But I commenced to wonder how even the mercurial Miss Jemima would manage to keep all these balls in the air at the same time. This was a most interesting development, one I had not seen happen before, and I wondered what would be the fall out of this faux pas? It was obvious Geoffrey's pride was severely dented. To the best of my knowledge Brickie didn't have any pride. Well, not much. But I could see the hurt and confusion and disappointment in his face and I observed that Brickie had already conceded that in a two horse race with Geoffrey Winters he would not be in the winner's enclosure this evening. If he intended to see *Gunfight at the O.K. Corral* it would be in the back stalls, and odds on not in the company of Miss Jemima.

This was undoubtedly a very tricky and awkward situation for both parties in our little group. We had a sort of unwritten code that no matter what happened, we never, not under any circumstances, undermined or attempted to cut out another member of our gang or allow his reputation to suffer loss. No matter what. I looked across at Geoffrey.

"How are you going to handle this, Geoffrey?"

Geoffrey pulled back the sleeve of his blazer and glanced at his timepiece. I took a look at my own watch which, having been purchased somewhere on Blackpool's Golden Mile, was of course nowhere near the class of the one sported by Geoffrey, but which by happy coincidence gave exactly the same time as his Rolex. Five minutes to six o'clock. Geoffrey looked up at Brickie. "Edward," he said slowly to the down-hearted layer of bricks, "shall we proceed to the Regent and ascertain if Miss Jemima is waiting for you to escort her to the *Gunfight at O.K. Corral?*"

Brickie, whose main interest in the evening, if truth be told, was to see Kirk Douglas and Burt Lancaster shoot up the baddies at the Corral, with or without Miss Jemima Muldoon, readily agreed. He rose to his feet and pushed back his chair. "Aye! We'll dander up to the Regent. And see if Miss Jemima is waitin for me!"

We bade Nancy farewell for the present and tumbled from the cafe as Connie Francis started to give out with *Everybody's Somebody's Fool* from the jukebox. We strode up Regent Street like the three musketeers – one for all and all for one – and I wondered what Miss Jemima's thoughts might be – if she was there – when her beautiful peepers beheld the cavalry bearing down upon her.

Miss Muldoon was not in attendance at the Regent. Neither did she make an appearance within the time-honoured two extra minutes always allotted for ladies privilege to be late, though this was a part of the game I never did wholeheartedly give my endorsement to believing as I do the old adage that punctuality is the politeness of kings with no exceptions being made, and not even for the likes of Miss Jemima Muldoon.

"Shall we proceed to the Ritz, Edward," Geoffrey asked politely.

"Aye. We'll proceed to the Ritz," agreed Brickie whose faint hopes of still being in the running for the affection of the fair Miss Jemima now disappeared like the horse he'd backed in the Grand National two or three weeks earlier. "We will proceed to the Ritz," he repeated, with no enthusiasm whatever.

Miss Jemima Muldoon was waiting at the Ritz; all dressed up like something out of a club book. Ah, but she was beautiful. A delight to behold. Although she had slipped a few points in my overall rating due to the plight in which she had placed my two buddies, all that was swept away when I again beheld her fair form. But a puzzled expression came over her film-star features as the three of us marched up to her, Geoffrey and Brickie leading the charge like something out of *The Quiet Man* and Dinger and myself bringing up the rear.

Miss Jemima's gaze of bewilderment alternated between Geoffrey and Brickie, as she stood transfixed to the spot. I could see she was trying in her pretty little head to work out some problem or mystery which had suddenly come her way and which she was in no way prepared for.

"Well, Edward," declared Geoffrey as we drew up beside the fair lady. "It is almost five minutes past six o'clock and here is Miss Jemima standing outside the Ritz. I understand you had an appointment to meet Miss Jemima at the Regent cinema at six o'clock this evening?"

Brickie nodded and grunted. Miss Jemima blushed and looked decidedly uncomfortable. "Obviously, Edward," continued Geoffrey, "Miss Jemima did not show at the Regent. Coincidentally, I myself have an appointment to meet the same lady right here at the Ritz at the very same time she was to meet you at the Regent." I personally had no idea where all this was leading but I entertained the hope it might lead somewhere pretty soon or I myself was going to miss the opening credits of *Gunfight at the O.K. Corral* and Frankie Laine singing the theme song. Geoffrey paused and made a sweeping bow to Miss Jemima. "Well, Edward, here she is, presumably to accompany me to the Ritz, though in light of recent evidence and the circumstances in which we unfortunately find ourselves I would hesitate to place a great deal of money on that being the case. In view of all this, I suddenly find I have no desire to spend any time in the company of Miss Jemima Muldoon. To save the lady further embarrassment, Edward, I step aside. You may have her!" Brickie, to his everlasting credit, and taking a lead from Geoffrey's masterful performance, suddenly discovered a little pride of his own and decided to make the best of a bad job whereby he would emerge from the whole fiasco with his head held high and earn the reputation as one of the very few men about town documented as having turned down the delectable Miss Jemima Muldoon.

"I want nothin' to do with her, Geoffrey." he retorted. "You can take her!"

As Miss Muldoon literally squirmed on the spot Geoffrey repeated in a very stylish and classy fashion, though there could be no misunderstanding the import of his words, he had better things to do with his time than waste it on Miss Muldoon. I observed a certain cutting edge to Geoffrey I failed to notice previously in his character though under the circumstances I did not judge him harshly for this. "I do thank you for your kind offer, Edward," stated Geoffrey. "But I have no further interest in the lady. But perhaps, gentlemen, we might enjoy a pleasant evening on the town. By ourselves?"

I felt genuinely sorry for Miss Jemima Muldoon as her beautiful mouth opened and closed in embarrassment and confusion and she tried vainly to explain she got the nights mixed up, the times wrong, the places wrong and several other things wrong and she meant no offence as Geoffrey made another gallant bow and wished her on behalf of himself and his companions the most pleasant of evenings.

When word got around of this debacle Miss Jemima Muldoon's reputation was suddenly shot to pieces. It was the talk of the town how she dated two fellas in the same town on the same night at the same time and how they both left her standing with nowhere to go and nobody to go with.

But there is another old adage of which I am very fond and which states 'it is an ill wind that blows nobody any good' and to this I can personally testify. Miss Muldoon was still the best looker in town. But due to a sudden lack of interest in Miss Jemima's charms and the cancellation of several outstanding commitments by her admirers I found myself moving at a fast rate of knots up the list of her would be suitors. I thought I would, considering that the ill wind seemed to be blowing in my favour, try again. Ask her out. For one night only. Just for a laugh. Just one night.

That was, as the crow flies, forty-seven years, two children, six grandchildren and two great grandchildren ago. Miss Muldoon is as beautiful as ever, though she is no longer a Miss and her name is no longer Muldoon but the same as mine. Which brings to mind another of the old adages of which I am very fond, "be careful about what you set your heart upon, for you shall surely achieve it." There is no doubt about it. Everything finally comes, as the other old adage says, to him who waits. Even Miss Muldoon.

A Visit from Linfield

Blue, I said to my wee nephew Mark, when he first started to take an interest in Irish League football and wanted to know all about Linfield, the best team in the whole country. What did I know about them, he had asked? Where did they come from? Had I ever seen them play? Well, I knew something of Linfield's background. And I certainly had seen them play. Instantly my memory sped back across the years to a never to be forgotten warm spring day in 1958 when the famous Blues played Ards at Castlereagh Park. That was a day I'll never forget. But to answer Mark's queries and questions, I started at the beginning, or as close to the beginning of the Linfield story as I could get.

Blue, I explained. Blue was the favourite colour of the folk who lived on Belfast's Shankill Road. I didn't know how the fascination for this particular colour evolved. But evolve it did. It was, and still is, held in the utmost esteem by the citizens of the Shankill. There is no other colour on the palette which serves to delight them so and cause their heart to beat just a little bit faster when they lay their eyes upon that most popular of all colours.

The folks of the Shankill were honest hard working citizens, loyal to Queen and Ulster and a football team named Linfield. They lived in neat little rows of back to back streets of two up and two down houses, each with an enclosed brick yard leading to the communal entry at the back. Every year, at a certain time of every year, each tiny yard was given a liberal coat of whitewash by the householder.

None of the little houses had a bathroom. The lavatory was in the yard. When nature called, the citizen of the Shankill did not indicate he wished to go to the bathroom, or even the lavatory. He simply stated he was going to the "yard". Everyone knew exactly what his intentions would be once he gained that place of sanctuary.

The bath was also in the yard, hanging from a nail on the white-washed wall opposite the lavatory. Beneath the bath lay the small mountain of coal which burned in the open grates and heated the little homes. Whether viewed from the front or the rear, or from above, every street looked exactly the same, for they were the same, rows and rows of little red brick boxes with names like Dundee Street, Aberdeen Street, Agnes Street and Sunderland Street. Maybe Pete Seeger had them in mind when he penned his famous song *Little Boxes*

The people of the Shankill Road were a proud people. And not without reason. Every house in every street was, for its tenant, nothing less than a little palace. The tiny windows always shone brightly and were cleaned every morning. There was never a speck of dust to be seen on the fine white lace curtains and the brass doorknockers were lovingly polished until they gleamed like gold. The people of the Shankill cared lovingly for their modest little homes, though they owned not so much as a brick of one of them. Though under no obligation to do so, they painted the front facade of their tiny dwellings at their own expense, usually by their own hand and always at the same time of year as they whitewashed the back yard. This was usually round about the beginning of the month of July. July was, and still is, a very important month for the people of the Shankill Road.

Some of the Shankill householders decorated the exterior of their little palaces in that most favourite of all favourite colours, blue. Some houses were painted red. Some were painted white. Most were decorated in a combination of all three colours, red, white and blue. Having painted the houses and made them so stunningly attractive the tenants always came to the unanimous conclusion it would be the height of folly to leave the kerbstones in their naturally drab colour of stone grey. So the kerbstones were painted. Red. White. And blue.

In the city of Belfast, much could be known about a man by the street in which he lived. If, for example, he happened to dwell in the aforementioned Dundee Street, Aberdeen Street, Agnes Street or Sunderland Street, it could safely be assumed his favourite colour was blue and he supported Linfield, the most successful football team in the Irish League now that Belfast Celtic were out of it.

Linfield football team was the pride and joy of the people of the Shankill Road. It was their reason for living. They loved it dearly. It was no coincidence therefore that the colour of the shirts the players of this fine team pulled on every Saturday afternoon was blue. Not pale blue. Not ice blue. Not even sky blue. But Royal Blue. How the people of the Shankill Road worshipped those Royal Blue shirts and the gallant men who wore them. And so it came to be, because of their great love for the colour blue and the fact that they supported Linfield who played in blue, the people of the Shankill Road in time came to be known collectively as "Bluemen".

That the Bluemen idolized their team there was no possible doubt. Linfield were far and away the best and most consistent team in the Irish League, bar none. Tommy Dickson, the "Duke of Windsor" played for them. So had "head, heel or toe, slip it to Joe" Bambrick, the "head, heel, or toe" meaning if a team-mate slipped the ball to Joe he would kindly use any part of his anatomy to stick it into the opposing team's net. "Wor Jackie" Milburn, the former idol of Newcastle United and Tyneside and prolific goal scorer, was also presently playing for Linfield. And where else were all the international football games played but at Windsor Park, home of the famous and dearly loved Linfield Football Club.

Linfield won every game of football they played. Well, almost every game. It had been known for the team to suffer a defeat. But this was such a rare event there were few people about the Shankill who could recall the last time it happened, or confess it ever did happen. Other football teams, even Glentoran, the wee Cock and Hens, who played beneath the stark shipyard gantries on the other side of Belfast, could be beaten, and often were, which was only to be expected. But the Bluemen, who for some unaccountable reason were also known as "The People", could never quite understand why, if the pun can be excused, once in the blue moon the magnificent team of Linfield suffered a defeat.

But the world is full of such unexplained mysteries. Sometimes the most unexpected disaster happened without warning and without rhyme or reason for it. So The People took extra special care to warn their tender offspring that it was just within the bounds of possibility that during their lifetime they might actually witness Linfield football team lose a game, lest the terrible event coming upon them unawares should sap their confidence and leave them with an inferiority complex for the rest of their lives. Some aged Glentoran supporters who claimed to have seen Linfield defeated, and even that their team had been the author of it, declared that when it happened every window blind on the Shankill Road was lowered for three days as a mark of mourning and respect.

Defeat however, was far from the minds or the thoughts of The People this Saturday as they emptied from their little streets on the warm April day. They paraded in droves across Belfast and into busy Royal Avenue, heading for High Street, Ann Street and the bus depot at the Sand Quay in Oxford Street. Today The People would enjoy a nice day out in the country. Their destination was the fair little town of Newtownards in the county of Down. They'd spent many a happy afternoon in Newtownards before, picking up full points from the Ards football team. They looked forward to more of the same today.

The afternoon was bright and sunny, the Bluemen relaxed and happy. They whistled and sang and carried their Linfield banners aloft and waved their scarves of red and white and blue above their head, rang hand bells and tooted their little plastic trumpets and tin horns. The bus run down to Newtownards and Castlereagh Park to play Ards would be a pleasant affair with another easy victory to boost the Blues charge toward the top of the league table, where they rightly belonged.

Belfast took on a carnival atmosphere as the mass of red, white and blue spilled on to the roads causing much annoyance to the drivers of motor cars and big red trolley buses. The happy blue army weaved through the city, a moving musical jingle jangle of song and dance and dire threats of what was about to happen to the Ards football team when the mighty Blues hit their town. Everywhere was blue. Rosettes, balloons, scarves, caps and huge banners suitably inscribed to inform those who may have been from another planet outside the presently known galaxy that these were The People, also known as Bluemen. And they were on a mission.

Linfield's number one supporter, the eccentric Lone Ranger, led the happy band of noise and colour across the city. The Lone Ranger was not a young man. He wasn't even a middle-aged man. He was an old man, a thin wiry character who dressed like and took his name from the television masked cowboy who wore a white Stetson and a black mask. Linfield's Lone Ranger also wore a cowboy hat, though his originated from a child's cowboy outfit and was black instead of white. He had acquired his black mask from Elliot's Self Hire on Ann Street. His ex-army greatcoat had been picked up from a pawn shop on the Albertbridge Road on a day when the Blues had travelled across to the Oval to trounce sworn enemies Glentoran. The toy gun belt slung around his waist held a supply of mock silver tipped bullets and in the star spangled holster nestled a plastic Colt 45 made in Chad and bought in Woolworth's.

The original television Lone Ranger always sat tall in the saddle. So did Linfield's pride and joy. Not on Silver, the original Lone Ranger's famous horse, but on Daisy, the almost as famous rusty sit up and beg black Raleigh bicycle. The big Raleigh had carried Linfield's Lone Ranger safely to every football ground in the Irish League and brought him home again. However, to far-flung grounds such as the Brandywell and the Coleraine Showgrounds, the bike travelled with the Lone Ranger in the comfort of a railway carriage and was only used for the run from the local train station down to the ground. The bike had two bells and no brakes, the absence of brakes making the two bells an absolute necessity. But when the Lone Ranger threw his leg over his machine and began to pedal, he didn't quit until he reached the ground where the Blues would play. He was harmless, one of the last of the old characters who supported the local game. He suffered much vocal abuse from opposing fans. But he gave as good as he got and all was given and taken in good natured banter. The Linfield Lone Ranger was more than welcome at whichever ground his Blue team played.

The Ranger was still at the head of the blue army as my mate Dinger Bell and myself watched the first wave of The People sweep into Newtownards at half past one, exactly one and a half hours before the big game kicked off. The Ranger pedalled erratically down Regent Street, steering the big bike with one hand and shooting the firing caps in his silver gun into the air and informing the bemused citizens on the street that The Lone Ranger and The People were in town.

Dinger and I watched the Blues storm in, bugles blowing and flags waving. The town had been under siege before from The

People and knew how to handle it. A few shops closed early. But most kept their doors wide open. The Bluemen were loud and vociferous, but the banter was good humoured and Linfield supporters weren't adverse to spending money on their way into the town and also on their way back out again. Dinger and I grinned as we watched the riot of colour and noise stream down the street, singing and cheering and jeering the Ards supporters. They swept on into the Square, many of them stopping to grab a fish supper in brown paper from Charlotte Heron's or one of the Cafollas' eating houses.

"We've no chance of beatin' this lot," grumbled Dinger. "I don't know why we bother goin' down to see it!"

"Give over," I grinned. "George Eastham is the best manager Ards has ever had. He's got the team playing some nice football."

"You can play nice football 'til the cows come home," muttered Dinger. "But it's goals that win football matches. And Linfield can score goals, no matter what sort of football they play!"

To cheer Dinger up I paid for two big sliders of ice-cream from Charlotte's. There was plenty of time before the game. We planked ourselves on a seat in front of the town hall and watched the hordes of noisy Bluemen take over the Square. We licked our sliders and debated what the result of this football match would be. It was a vital game. For both teams. Somewhat unexpectedly, Ards found themselves near the top of the League. Linfield were also thereabouts, which was only to be expected. They usually lifted the league title year after year. Most Ards fans reckoned the Newtownards side would be on the wrong end of the score line when this game was over. Dinger was absolutely certain of it. We finished our ice-creams and mingled with the blue army as it flowed into High Street, past the War Memorial at the Bowling Green and on down the Portaferry Road toward Castlereagh Park.

"Luk at that!" complained Dinger as we strolled past Castle Gardens School on the final leg of the dander down to the Park. Half a dozen Linfield supporters' buses had just swept past. Each bus was packed with scores of Linfield fans. "There's millions of them!" cried my mate. "Millions of them! We've no chance!"

The buses roared past. Linfield scarves and banners flew triumphantly from every window, their owners treated to rousing cheers of welcome from the gangs of their fellow supporters as they danced and sang their way to the football ground. The Bluemen enjoyed coming down to Castlereagh Park. The pitch was reckoned to be the finest in all Ireland. The playing surface was as smooth as a billiard table and someone had once said that if a player couldn't play football at Castlereagh Park he couldn't play football anywhere. Even the Linfield supporters grudgingly acknowledged it "wasn't bad."

The Bluemen were ebullient and in great spirit as they queued at the turnstiles. The Ards supporters were quiet and apprehensive. They had every reason to be. Their record against Linfield wasn't good. It was terrible. Ards played good football – very good football. But they were goal-shy. Linfield had players who could score from twenty or thirty yards, turning half chances into goals. Ards didn't. "We're in for a real hammerin'," moaned Dinger as he slammed down his one and ninepence. "We'll not get a kick at it! It's lucky for us Milburn's injured and won't be playin'."

I grinned. "It's eleven against eleven. We can play football just as good as they can."

"We can't score goals like they can," snorted Dinger as we pushed our way into the unreserved side of the ground. "They can score from anywhere. Not us. Manager Eastham wants our team to walk the ball up to the goalkeeper, shake hands with him and ask if he'd mind awfully if we tapped it into his net!"

I laughed. Dinger had a point. Eastham was a soccer purist. A former England international, he had transformed the Ards team when he was brought over to manage the County Down club. Eastham did indeed believe in playing the ball up to and into the opposing team's net, much to the frustration of the Ards fans who often advised their forward line when they neared goal to "hit it a kick!" It was this lack of killer punch, the one thing Linfield had in abundance, which bothered the Ards fans today. Dinger and I filed our way in and took up our usual position against the low wall at the half way line. This gave us a good view of the game wherever the play might be. The turnstiles clicked repeatedly as more and more Linfield and Ards fans flowed into the Park, the Blue supporters to collect two easy points and Ards fans praying for a miracle.

The sun was warm upon my face as it continued to beam down brightly from the clear blue sky high above Scrabo. I felt good and for a moment I mentally entertained the thought that maybe we could hold the mighty Linfield to a draw. That would be a tremendous achievement. I looked up as a couple of light planes buzzed overhead, taking off and landing beyond the corrugated fence at the airport end of the ground and providing a bit of excitement for the multitude of Blue fans.

The Stars and Stripes Forever scratchily belted out from the loudspeakers around the compact little ground as I breathed in the smell of newly mown grass on the immaculate pitch. The soft green turf was ideally suited to the Ards team who'd been coached to keep the ball on the ground and play in tight little triangles. Football, insisted manager Eastham. The name of the game was football. Play it on the ground. Always football. I glanced across the pitch to the corner flags. They hung limply. There wasn't a breath of a breeze to assist or impede either team. Win, loose, or draw, there would be no excuse for either side.

At ten minutes to three The Stars and Stripes Forever was unceremoniously cut from the Ards P.A. system. Ards secretary Harry Cavan gave a couple of hearty puffs into the microphone to ensure his voice would be heard above the loud buzz around the ground. "Good afternoon, ladies and gentlemen," Harry voiced in his immaculate tones. "Welcome to Castlereagh Park. Here are the teams for today's game. Ards – Smyth, Hunter, McGuicken, Forde, Giffen, Cummings, Humphries, Richardson, Lawther, Lowry, McDonnell." The Ards fans groaned. Their main strike force against the mighty Blues was to be wee Davie Lawther. Five foot nothing Davie Lawther, who could miss a goal from two feet out, was to play at centre forward against Linfield's six foot three centre half Tommy Hamill. Tommy was rock solid in the heart of the Linfield defence. He took no prisoners. It didn't bear thinking about. "And the Linfield team," continued Harry when the groans died down. "Russell, Gilliland, Graham, Rodgers, Hamill, Gough, Fisher, Parke, Robinson, Dickson, Braithwaite. The referee is Mr Arthur Ellis."

When it seemed not another single supporter of either persuasion could be squeezed into Castlereagh Park a tremendous roar reverberated around the ground as Linfield ran on to the pitch. The team were absolutely resplendent in their Royal Blue shirts, white pants and blue socks. They oozed fitness and energy and determination and confidence as they took the applause and cheers of their supporters.

"Come on the mighty Blues!" howled The People enthusiastically as their team stroked the ball about at the airport end of the ground and waited for Ards to come out. "Get intil these hillybillies!"

Their captain and former Linfield player, Geordie Richardson, led out Ards. The polite applause from the Ards supporters was drowned out by the boos, jeers and catcalls of The People. Dinger and I, who now found ourselves surrounded by vociferous Bluemen, clapped all the louder. I gave Dinger a dunt with my elbow as the jeers of the Bluemen died away and Geordie Richardson and the Linfield captain trotted to the centre circle for the toss of the referee's coin to choose ends.

"I think we'll beat them, Dinger," I said.

"An' I'm goin' to win the pools!" retorted Dinger. "Eight draws. One after the other. All in a row. Seventy-five thousand smackers! Are ye right in the head? The only way we'll beat this lot is if they score an own goal for us then go into the pavilion and don't come out again. Luk at them! We're goin' to get hammered!"

—— ∞ ——

"Don't bet on it," I laughed. "This could be the upset of the day."

"Upset m' fut!" snorted Dinger. "It'll be an upset if they don't stick six past us. And if we did beat them, you'd have half this crowd chuckin' themselves into the Lagan on the way home!"

"I still think we'll win," I insisted. "It's got to happen sometime. This is as good a day as any."

"Dream on!" grumbled Dinger as the teams lined up for the start of the game.

A hush of anticipation fell over the ground. I could feel the tension between both sets of supporters, even among the players, as the referee signalled to his linesmen. We were about to find out if Ards deserved their place near the top of the Irish League or were destined to go crashing in free fall in the other direction. Linfield desperately needed the points to maintain their challenge for yet another trophy. It was all to play for.

The referee checked his watch. He raised the whistle to his mouth. Then he removed it again, much to the annoyance of the Bluemen who were more than anxious for the slaughter to begin.

"Blow the whistle, ref!" bawled The Lone Ranger from the middle of the Linfield supporters just behind us. "It's nearly lightin' up time! I've no lights for my bicycle! Blow the whistle, or throw it over here and I'll blow it for ye!"

The referee heard the Lone Ranger's voice cut through the silence and tension. He looked across to the terraces and smiled. But he thought it might possibly be in the best interests of the game if he himself blew the whistle. At exactly three o'clock he did so. I took a deep breath. This was it. The big match.

The Big Match

Linfield swept into the attack immediately, an all out blitzkrieg heading straight for the Ards goal. This delighted the Linfield supporters and brought groans of consternation from the Ards fans.

"What did I tell ye," moaned my mate Dinger. "They're goin' to murder us! Let me outa here!"

"Give over," I laughed. "The match is only started."

"Don't I know it," sighed Dinger. "Only eighty nine minutes of torture to go!"

Dinger had just finished speaking when the Blues forced a corner down their right wing. Fisher, the Linfield outside right, flighted a beautiful ball across the Ards goalmouth just beyond the flailing hands of the veteran Ards goal-keeper Billy Smyth. The Linfield inside left, Tommy Dickson, popularly known by Bluemen as The Duke Of Windsor, steamed in from beyond the penalty area and headed the ball straight for the top corner of the Ards net.

"Goal!" screamed The People with one voice. And goal it would have been if the Ards left back Ralph McGuicken, a former Linfield player, hadn't popped up from nowhere and headed the ball from under the crossbar and out of play for a throw in.

The cheers died in the throats of the Bluemen. They did not at all appreciate the action of the Ards full-back, which had denied them a dream start to the game. It irked them even more that Ralph had at one time worn the famous blue shirt.

"You're only a has-been, McGuicken!" roared a Linfield supporter from just behind us. "That's why we got rid of you. Get away back to the farm and weed the turnips. You know nothin' about football!"

Dinger, who had the misfortune to be standing closest to the loudest of the Bluemen turned and glared at the football philosopher. The fat little man sported an eagle nose decorated by a pair of National Health spectacles, one leg of which was secured to the lens by a piece of ragged sellotape. A Glasgow Rangers scarf was draped around his neck and a Linfield rosette hung in the lapel of his anorak. Upon his head he sported a blue and white paper hat bearing the legend "Linfield for the Cup". "Better a has-been than a never-was, like that lot playin' for you," growled Dinger. "And Ralph knew enough about football to keep the ball out of the net. That's good enough for us."

The rebuked Linfield philosopher adjusted his spectacles, especially where the sellotape had come loose, to get a better view of Dinger. "Listen, fella. If McGuicken's goin' to head out everything we throw at him in this match he's goin' to have a sore head before this game's over!"

"You might be surprised who has the sore head when the game's over," retorted Dinger as his heckles started to rise.

"That's the style, Dinger," I laughed, "I knew all along you fancied Ards to beat them!"

Dinger snorted. "You've got to be jokin'. It's as plain as the nose on your face they're goin' to hammer us. But we might as well do a bit of shoutin' while we're still level with them. We'll not get a chance to do it later on."

It seemed Dinger was correct. Wave upon wave of relentless Linfield attacks beat down on the Ards defence in the first few minutes of the match. I winced with the rest of the Ards faithful as the ball clipped our crossbar, struck an upright, or was unceremoniously booted away for another corner kick. Billy Smyth performed acrobatic miracles in the Ards goal as he and the rest of the Ards players tried everything they knew to prevent a Linfield goal.

"Come on the Blues!" roared the knot of Linfield supporters standing around Dinger and myself. "Get bogged into these farmers!"

"Come on Ards!" bawled Dinger. "If it wasn't for us farmers these slum dwellers wouldn't have any milk to put in their tea!"

The People were not at all delighted to be referred to as slum dwellers. The situation was just about to turn somewhat ugly and was only temporarily delayed as Linfield's Duke of Windsor bore down on the Ards goal for the umpteenth time. I held my breath as the Linfield hit-man blasted in a fierce shot from fully twenty five yards. The ball was travelling at a fierce rate of knots on its way into our goal. Really travelling. On his day the Ards goalkeeper, Billy Smyth, was as good as any goalie in the country. But he was beaten all ends up as the ball fairly smashed against the underside of his crossbar and rebounded on to the goal-line. Dessie Hunter, the Ards right-back, reacted immediately and did what a good full-back is supposed to do in such a situation. He cleared his lines. Dessie booted the ball high into the grandstand on the un-reserved part of the ground.

"Goal!" screeched the Bluemen. "Goal! Ref, it's a goal!"

The rules of Association Football state clearly a goal may only be awarded when the whole of the ball has passed over the whole of the goal-line, everything else being in order. For the frustrated Bluemen it was definitely more than sufficient that the ball had hit the underside of the bar and dropped on to the goal-line. There could only have been two or three inches in it anyway. Again they screamed for a goal at the same time taking the opportunity to question the referee's eyesight, or lack of it.

The referee looked across to his linesman for clarification. That gentleman, which was not what the Linfield supporters called him, kept his flag well and truly down and waved play on. The exact relationship of the linesman to his paternal mother and father was immediately called into question by The People who it appeared had some inside information on the matter.

"Never a goal," Dinger whooped delightedly to nobody in particular. "The whole of the ball has to be over the line!"

"The whole of the ball was over the line," snarled he of the sellotape glasses. "The line's bendy! If it was a straight line the ball would have been over it. It's a conspiracy! It's a conspiracy!"

"Away and get your glasses fixed, Shorty," smirked Dinger as he turned to face the Blueman. "The referee is closer to it than you. And he said it wasn't a goal." At this point Shorty's mate, a skinny youth about twice the height of Shorty and sporting an Elvis For President legend on his blue paper hat, joined the fray. "Listen, mate," he bristled. "There's no need to be insultin'. It was a good goal. That referee is playin' for youse. He's playin' for youse!"

"He's not playin' for us," laughed Dinger. "We're doin' all right on our own. And we're just gettin' warmed up. Wait to you see what happens when we really get goin'!"

I kicked Dinger's ankles. "Let them alone. You know what they're like when they don't get their own way. You'll start a riot here!"

Dinger wouldn't be silenced. "I'll rub it into them while I can. If they get a goal they'll let us know all about it." He cupped his hands to his mouth and bawled across the pitch at the top of his voice. "Come on Ards! Get into these donkeys. They couldn't score in a month of Sundays!"

It may have been coincidence. Or it may have been that the Ards team noted Dinger's words of encouragement. They began to realise the Linfield team was nowhere near as indestructible as they imagined. Suddenly they began to take the odd excursion into the Blues' half of the field. Once or twice they made Russell, the Linfield goalkeeper, come out to make a save. This was something the Linfield fans were not at all used to. Much to their annoyance the other Ards fans took up Dinger's rallying cry and advised Ards to ease off and give the Blues a kick at the ball, or at the very least, a little look at it.

Then something not one person in the entire ground expected to see, happened. After yet another all out Linfield attack, that most reliable and cultured of full-backs, Ralph McGuicken, booted the ball off the Ards goal-line. It landed at the feet of wee Billy Humphries out on the Ards right wing. Billy blinked as the ball landed at his feet. Until this point in the game it had never come anywhere near him. To pass the time he had been reduced to taking a very keen interest in the plant life around his own particular patch of pitch, away from all the action. When the ball landed at his feet he wasn't quite sure how it had found its way to him from the Ards goalmouth. But Billy was a fine player. And a quick thinker. He glanced across the pitch to where his inside right Geordie Richardson was bearing down on the Linfield goal. "Go, Billy! Go!" cried Geordie. Billy did. He galloped right up to the Blues left-back. He feinted to cut inside the Linfield man and then left him kicking empty space as he danced past him on the outside and cut back an inch perfect cross. Richardson met the ball at full gallop and crashed it against the Linfield post with the keeper beaten all ends up.

"Thought it was in!" groaned Dinger as he clutched his head in his hands. But good news was on the way. Dinger lowered his hands just in time to see the ball bounce back from the Blues post and roll into the perfect position for tiny Ards centre-forward Davie Lawther to skip past big Tommy Hamill the Blues centre-half as if he wasn't there and lash the loose ball well and truly into the back of the Linfield net. I'll never forget that moment. It's etched on my mind to this very day. If someone had dropped a pin in Castlereagh Park every person in the ground would have heard it. The Linfield supporters could not believe what they were looking at. Neither could we. The ball lay in the back of their net. Their goalkeeper, Alex Russell, who up to now hadn't even been called upon to make a decent save, lay sprawled on the ground beside it. And the Ards fans were no less stunned than the Bluemen. Only in dreamland did such things happen when Ards played Linfield. Cautiously, with baited breath, the eyes of every Ards supporter turned from the ball lying in the Linfield net to Mr Ellis the referee. Could it really be a goal?

The referee didn't hesitate. He blew his whistle and pointed to the centre spot. Goal! Ards had scored. Dinger danced a jig, a samba, the hokey-kokey and every other type of dance movement known to man as every Ards supporter in the ground went delirious with joy. If there had been a roof on Castlereagh Park it would have lifted clean off as applause, cheers, whoops and whistles of appreciation erupted from every part of the stadium, except where the Bluemen congregated. The Linfield supporters were shocked into open mouthed silence as their players stood with hands on hips and stared dejectedly at their goalkeeper and the ball lying in the back of their net.

"Come on the eleven farmers!" roared Dinger hoarsely. "Come on the farmers! Get bogged into these city slickers! Show them how the game should be played!" He turned and thumped me in the ribs, taking my breath away. "If this isn't worth a week's pay I don't know what is! Aw, if we could only hold on to this for a while! Luk at the faces behind you! Luk at them!"

I turned. The Bluemen still hadn't moved a muscle. Not one of The People had yet uttered a single word. The Lone Ranger ripped his Stetson from his head and flung it to the ground and danced on it in disgust. But no words came from his mouth. Shorty appeared to be gasping for air. His mouth opened and closed silently like a herring stranded on the harbour at Portavogie as he gallantly clutched for any straw to bring some sense of perspective to the calamity which had just befallen his team and its supporters.

"It wasn't a goal!" he guldered. "Lawther was offside! He was offside!" Dinger turned to face the squawking Blueman. "How was he offside? Didn't he run past your centre-half before he hit the ball? Away and get yer glasses fixed and read the rules!"

"Well, our goalie should have come off his line quicker than he did," mumbled Shorty's mate as he thrust his hands deep into his pockets. "He should have saved it. Then it wouldn't have been a goal!"

There was no answer to this priceless piece of philosophy. Even Dinger didn't bother to respond. He turned again to watch the play. Suddenly there was a lack of confidence in the Linfield team. The Ards score had rattled them. And it showed. They mounted attack after attack but still couldn't get the ball into the Ards net. This gave Ards and their supporters even more encouragement and provided more frustration for The People who began to turn on their own team. Suddenly Tommy Dickson, whose name they had chanted and lauded as the best goal-scorer in the land, was advised by his own supporters to go home and get his feet turned and if possible to call in at the opticians on the way back for a pair of spectacles which might enable him to see exactly where the Ards goal was. The Linfield manager was criticised for playing players out of position and for not buying a decent striker when it was plain for everyone to see that was what the team had needed for months. The referee was a local, although he lived in England, and was playing for Ards. Worst of all, it was obvious for everyone in the ground to see that the Ards players were actually taking the ball away from the Linfield players, which was a very unsporting thing to do, and made it even more difficult for the Blues to score.

Ards grew visibly in stature after wee Davie hammered in their spectacular and totally unexpected goal. Now they stroked the ball about with a skill and confidence that surprised even Dinger and myself. It was Linfield who were doing all the desperate defending and completely unable to set up a meaningful attack of their own. When they did move on the Ards goal the Ards defence clinically snuffed out the threat and fed their own forward line once again. Humphries owned the right wing. He was turning in a sparkling performance feeding his inside right as well as laying balls off to wee Davie in the middle of the forward line. The diminutive Davie was running rings round big Tommy Hamill the Linfield centre half. Tommy was one of the best defenders in the league. But wee Davie wasn't giving him a look-in.

The Ards forward line was really buzzing. Davie drifted out to the wing. Big Tommy didn't know whether to follow him or stay where he was. Humphries, who himself had a powerful shot and was no bigger than wee Davie, flitted in to fill Davie's centre-forward position and give big Tommy even more of a headache. The Ards players interchanged again, just after Linfield launched another all out effort to break down the Ards defence.

Most of the Linfield team were still in the Ards half of the pitch after another raid when it happened. Wee Davie picked up an inch perfect pass from Humphries and headed straight for Linfield's goal. Much to the delight of the Ards supporters and the dismay of the Bluemen, he easily beat Ray Gough, the Linfield half-back, and made a bee-line for big Tommy. Big Tommy was a great player in the air. But he couldn't deal with wee terrier Davie tripping in around his ankles. Unwilling to commit himself, Tommy back-pedalled toward his own goal as Davie came at him.

Davie ran the ball right up to big Tommy. He feinted to go left. Desperately Tommy stuck out a foot in that direction. The ball wasn't there. Neither was Davie. Tommy sprawled on the ground as Davie danced away and closed in on the Linfield keeper. "Foul!" roared the Lone Ranger and the rest of the Bluemen with one voice. "Foul, ref! He kicked big Tommy! It's a foul!" The referee ignored the claims of the enraged Bluemen as Davie beheld the whites of the Linfield goalie's eyes. Dinger and I held our breath. Davie was the type of player who could score from the most difficult of positions. But he usually failed miserably when all he had to do was tap the ball into an empty net. Now he'd worked himself into the easiest of all goal-scoring opportunities. He had only the goalkeeper to beat. Beyond Russell lay the defenceless Linfield net.

"Shoot, Davie! Shoot!" roared Dinger and at least one half of Castlereagh Park. The tiny centre-forward didn't bother trying to waltz round the Linfield keeper. He didn't try to lob him. He didn't even look up to see where he was. He took Dinger's advice and simply blasted the ball past the keeper so hard the goalie didn't even see it. It struck the back of the net with such force it almost tore a hole in it before it dropped and rolled into the bottom corner.

The Ards supporters were sent spinning crazily into a delirium of delight and euphoria. Two goals up against Linfield! Unbelievable! Dinger and I cheered and whooped until we were hoarse. We hugged and danced with practically every Ards supporter on the terracing, male or female. We clapped and cheered and laughed and taunted the Bluemen with even more conviction than when Ards scored their first goal.

"Foul!" shrieked the Bluemen, foul being their instant response at any stage of the game when things weren't going exactly the way they'd expected. And this game most certainly was not going the way they'd expected when they'd left the dear streets of the Shankill Road for Newtownards town. "Foul, referee!" they screeched. "Foul! Lawther kicked big Tommy! He kicked him!" But the referee had already blown his whistle for the goal. He pointed to the centre circle as the Ards team lapped up the applause and adulation of their ecstatic fans. Unable to influence the referee to disallow the Ards goal, the Bluemen launched into a torrent of abuse aimed directly at the official with the whistle. "You couldn't referee a dog fight, ref! You're a disgrace to the game! How much is Ards payin' you? You know nothin' about the game!" bawled Shorty.

Dinger turned. He gave Shorty and his frustrated Blue companions one of his widest grins. "He's an appointed referee. He's wearin' the badge to prove it."

"He must have bought it in Woolworth's," complained Shorty's mate bitterly. "It's the only way he could have got it. He knows nothin' about refereein'. And the only way youse were able to score against us was when all our players was at the other end of the field. We're gettin' robbed here! We're gettin' robbed!"

Dinger and I both knew, and so did every other Ards supporter in the ground, that Linfield football team were always at their most dangerous when they were hurt. And they were hurt now. Badly. For the rest of the first half they peppered the Ards goal with shots from all over the park. But when Mr Ellis blew his whistle for half time they still hadn't found the Ards net. Dinger rubbed his hands gleefully. He slapped me on the back as the two teams made their way into the pavilion. "What a performance! Two up! Against the Blues! If only we could hold on to this. Aw! If only we could!" I nodded. This was far more than I had ever dreamed of. More than any Ards fan had any right to expect. We couldn't have asked for better. But I tried to calm my mate.

"Don't get carried away, Dinger. We're doing great. But you know Linfield. Never beaten until the fat lady sings. And she's only half way through the chorus! We need to hold this for a full forty-five minutes!"

Linfield began the second half the way they ended the first. It was a real embarrassment for them to be two goals down against a country team like Ards. They came out determined to haul back the deficit and then go on to win the game. Attack after attack rained down on the Ards goal. The Linfield forward line bombarded the Ards keeper with shots from every angle and position and I don't think Dinger and I were the only Ards supporters in the ground who had bitten their nails into the quick. But the Ards defence stood strong. They dealt with everything the Blues threw at them and with several apple-cores and a few showers of orange peel their supporters tossed in for good measure.

As the clock ticked slowly but relentlessly on the Blues began to fade as an attacking force. The Castlereagh Park side again came more and more into the game and then began to dominate it, playing superb close football exactly the way their manager Eastham demanded. They ran rings round the Blues. Linfield still made chances. But they couldn't convert them into goals.

The Ards forward line swept down once more on the Linfield goal. A tremendous Billy Humphries shot brought a superb save from the Linfield keeper. Unfortunately the goalie, in his haste to get the ball as far away from his net as possible, accidentally booted it off the back of his own centre-half's head. Big Tommy fell to the ground, spark out.

"Foul," bawled Shorty.

"Foul!" roared every Blueman in the ground. Dinger and I turned and laughed at the distraught Bluemen.

"How's it a foul?" demanded Dinger of Shorty. "Didn't I tell you to get them glasses fixed? Or if you can't get them fixed, take them off altogether so you can see what's goin' on! It was your own goalkeeper who hit him. Get a grip of yourself!"

Big Tommy recovered from the accidental biff on the head from his own team-mate. But with twenty minutes to go The People, sad, miserable and dejected, had yet one more indignity to suffer. Wee Davie Lawther again found himself all alone in the penalty area after weaving pretty circles round big Tommy who was having one of those games he wouldn't want to look back on with any degree of pride or read about in Ireland's Saturday Night later on in the evening.

"Offside!" screamed Shorty.

"Offside!" screeched the Lone Ranger and the rest of the Bluemen.

Shorty was wrong. Again. So was the venerable Lone Ranger and several thousand other Bluemen in the ground. The silky footballing skills of the Ards forward line had left Davie in another of those positions we didn't like to see him in. An easy tap in for a goal. So easy I could score it myself. But another of those chances Davie usually blasted high, wide and handsome over the bar and out on to the Portaferry Road and half way up Gallows Hill. But Davie didn't disappoint. Without looking up he coolly slipped the ball under the diving Russell and into the far corner of the net. Game over. To this day there are folk who were as far away as Ballywalter and Greyabbey and Millisle and even Portavogie who swear they heard the cheer from Castlereagh Park when Davie's third goal hit the back of the Linfield net. Not many Linfield supporters heard it. Most of them had evacuated from the ground the instant the ball left wee Davie's boot, led by the Lone Ranger who was already pedalling furiously past the Bowling Green bar on his rusty Raleigh.

"Robbery! Highway robbery!" he screamed angrily to every one who would listen as he wobbled erratically up the road waving his toy six-gun in the air. "Daylight robbery! At least Dick Turpin had the dacecny to wear a mask! But not here! Down here they rob you bare-faced! We were robbed! Robbed! Iverybody's out to get Linfield!"

And so the Bluemen returned, disconsolately, to find refuge and succour in their little homes on the Shankill Road. Their visit to Newtownards town, a visit that had started off so well and so full of promise and enjoyment, had turned into a humiliating disaster. They were defeated. And downhearted. But not for long. They were Bluemen. Win, loose, or draw, they were Bluemen. They were The People, supporters of Linfield Football Club. Next week at Windsor Park, their home ground, or wherever the Blues would play, they would be there, led into battle by the never-say-die Lone Ranger. They would win many, many more games than they would ever lose. And, as they confessed that Saturday night, when tempers cooled and common sense prevailed, it really was no disgrace to lose to a fine footballing side like Ards. The Castlereagh Park outfit, boosted by their great win over Linfield, went on to lift the Irish League title for the first time in their history.

Blue is still the favourite colour of the folk who live on Belfast's Shankill Road. But now the little palaces are gone, levelled to make way for a modern society. The Lone Ranger long ago rode off into the sunset to seek that great football pitch in the sky.

But his spirit lives on, as does the crack and banter and humour which abounds wherever Linfield play. It's a different game now. A different age. But the new modern houses are still home to the faithful who live and work and play around the Shankill. Windsor Park stands as proud as ever, home to Linfield football team and its supporters. Linfield is still the team to beat.

Maybe there aren't too many Linfield supporters who recall it. But there are plenty of old Ards supporters who do. I'm one of them. I was there. At Castlereagh Park. That April day in 1958, when mighty Linfield came to town. And Ards, playing George Eastham's silky football, trounced the invincible Blues. Three goals to nil. In the big match.

The Carrowdore Henhouse

My first motor car was a henhouse. Well, it wasn't a henhouse when it rolled off the Ford assembly line at their plant in Dagenham. But it was a henhouse when I first laid eyes on it about twenty years later, lying in a field a mile or two outside Carrowdore.

Not that I had any particular interest in the henhouse when I first saw it. Living in Robert Street in Newtownards, I was no longer a teenager. I was a married man with a wife and new family. But I didn't have any chickens about me that were in need of shelter and I certainly had no interest whatsoever in motor cars. Couldn't afford one. I was working as maintenance-joiner in the Regent Factory at the time, right beside the bus-station in Regent Street. The carpet king, Cyril Lord, owned it. *Luxury You Can Afford, By Cyril Lord.* That was Cyril's advertising catchphrase when he manufactured and flogged the carpets his workers churned out day and night in Donaghadee. If you bought a Cyril Lord carpet Cyril threw in a free bedspread as a bit of a bonus. The punters never seemed to twig on that Cyril had already added the price of the bedspread on to the price of the carpet. As the old adage says, there is no such thing as a free lunch. But it was our job to make the bedspreads in the Regent Street factory and post the already paid for free gifts to Cyril's carpet customers.

Regent Factory was a holiday camp. It was the closest thing to Butlins I've ever seen, the only real difference being they paid us to go to it instead of us paying them to let us in. But Cyril Lord did know a thing or two about luxury, as he claimed in his advertisements. Once in the blue moon, when he wasn't sunning himself in Florida or hosting a soirée at the Culloden, he'd drive up to the factory in a big Bentley half the length of a bus. He knew about luxury. But the eight quid a week Cyril was paying me to help make his bedspreads never brought me within sighting distance of the practical side of luxury. I rode to work on a second hand bicycle.

However, my old mate Dinger Bell, who was the factory mechanic, was never without half a dozen wrenches and two or three oily rags in his fists. He was motor car mad. He actually owned one. Well he would own it in three years when he'd finished the payments. Dinger's car was, or apparently at one time had been, according to the logbook, a Ford Eight. But Dinger had patched its body so many times with huge amounts of Isopon and tacked on so many second-hand and home-made parts of varying degrees of pedigree and quality, that it was unlikely describing the car as an authentic Ford Eight would have passed the Trades Description Act if Dinger ever took the notion of advertising it for sale. Not that he had any notion of selling, even though his moneybox on wheels was on the blink again.

"Nothin' serious," shrugged Dinger as we got stuck in to our lumps of soda bread and cheese during our ten-minute tea break one Saturday morning. "It's the battery. It's jiggered." Well, he didn't exactly say jiggered. But that's what he meant. "It's okay on

———— ∞ ————

a good mornin'. But if there's a touch of frost at all she'll not give a kick. Not even a spark. I can't depend on her."

"Why don't you get a new battery," I suggested.

Dinger glowered at me. "D'ye think I'm made of money! Have ye any idea what a battery costs?"

When I confessed my ignorance on such matters Dinger informed me a new battery would probably cost almost as much as he had originally paid for his automobile in the first place. "But I think I'm in luck," he exclaimed. "I read in the *Chronicle* that a fella out near Carrowdore has an oul Ford Eight he's sellin' for parts. He says the battery's in good order. Will you come out with me to take a luk at it?"

Well, I had no social engagements arranged for that particular evening so I said I would accompany Dinger, if his wee Ford would start, out to the green hills of Carrowdore to view the battery.

That was the first time I had availed myself of a ride in Dinger's pride and joy. I wished I hadn't bothered. The car was a wreck. How the whole thing held together in one piece, despite Dinger's Herculean efforts with rivets and Isopon and paint, was beyond me. The window winders didn't work. As a result the windows were jammed solid, right down in the open position. Dinger informed me this was a stroke of extremely good fortune. It enabled both himself and his passenger to give hand signals in lieu of the indicators, which had developed a temporary fault that last week had almost got him wiped out in the execution of a right turn before he was aware of their malfunction. There was a hole in the exhaust. Dinger said he could easily fix it with a bandage when he had a bit of time. Until then the holes in the floor afforded an opportunity for the escaping fumes from the faulty exhaust to permeate the inside of the vehicle and almost suffocate us before we had a chance to lay eyes on the green hills of Carrowdore. Upon my mentioning, albeit in a light-hearted fashion, that he seemed to be crossing the white lines on an unusually large number of occasions when going round corners, Dinger informed me the brakes needed shod but not to worry as he was a past master at driving on the gears and using them to slow the vehicle and anyway a really good driver didn't need brakes. But he would definitely get the lights fixed before winter set in.

Dinger navigated his ancient banger out beyond Carrowdore Castle, more or less keeping her between the hedges for most of the journey while I bounced about like a ping-pong ball on the lump of foam rubber Dinger had pinched from the factory to make a passenger seat. After getting lost on more than one occasion he finally steered up a long hilly lonen just off the Kilbright Road. Dinger pulled up to a halt outside the front door of a dilapidated farmhouse surrounded with broken down carts, buckets, food-troughs, the skeleton of a big green Fordson tractor and the remnants of an old mattress which was being utilised by a couple of collies who barely raised their head as we clambered out of the Ford.

"How're ye doin'," breezed Dinger to the oul fella in dungarees and peaked cap who pulled open the door in answer to his knock. "You have an oul' motor battery for sale?"

"Indeed I have," agreed the hayseed. "An' a dacent one it is. It's over thonder."

Dinger and I followed the general direction of the oul' fella's finger which pointed somewhere beyond the green hills of Carrowdore and across the blue Irish Sea to the purple hills of bonnie Scotland.

"Where exactly is that?" queried Dinger who obviously hadn't bargained on a boat trip to the land of bagpipes in his quest to secure a battery for his wee Ford.

"Over thonder," reiterated the farmer still pointing. "In thon field. Unner the hedge. Alongside the dung heap." Dinger and I had obviously aimed our sights a little too high. We lowered our eyes until they settled on a heap of rusted red metal which appeared to be the meeting place and possibly maternal home for a couple of dozen Rhode Island Reds, two or three bantys and a muscovi duck. "It's over thonder," confirmed the farmer. "Still in the motor. I was usin' the wee car for a hen house. She's in good order. But I'm sellin' her for parts. Do ye want to have a luk at her?"

I was about to declare I had no particular interest in looking at her. Hen houses, motorised or not, held no particular attraction for me. But Dinger and the hayseed were already half away across the field, which according to the smell in my nose suggested somebody had just finished scaling with dung.

The farmer cursed and shouted and shooed and waved the indignant hens and bantys and mucovi from the innermost recesses of the aged Ford. The car was in such an awful state it made Dinger's pride and joy look as if it had just been driven out from Harry Ferguson's motor showroom in Belfast. The farmer dragged open the protesting driver's door. He reached a hand into the manure-covered seat and picked up a single egg. He examined the egg in great detail then gave it a quick rub on his chest and with a smile slipped it into his dungaree pocket. He shuffled round to the front of the heap of scrap and pulled up the bonnet. Thanks to the quality of the rust on the bonnet's hinges he didn't have to prop it up. It just hung suspended where he had pushed it, defying gravity. The farmer pointed to the engine compartment after he'd wiped away the cobwebs and the remains of a lately vacated bird's nest. "Dacent wee battery. Take it away with ye for a couple of quid. Or tow the whole lot away for a fiver. She was a grand wee motor in her day. The hens and the ducks have lived in it for long enough. But I think she's past it now. I'll be gettin' a new house for the birds."

Dinger seemed to have temporarily lost interest in the battery. He wandered slowly around the vehicle. He kicked the tyres, bounced the suspension - well, tried to bounce the suspension - and got down on his knees and peered under the chassis. He rose to his feet and reached inside, hitting the switches for the lights and windscreen wipers. To Dinger's obvious delight the lights beamed on immediately and the wipers struggled into life and smudged the layer of chicken droppings all over the windscreen.

Dinger turned to me. He pointed to the henhouse. "Could you drive that thing home?"

I laughed in his face. "Don't be daft! You're not allowed to drive a henhouse on the road. It's not legal."

"I don't mean drive it," snorted Dinger. "I mean steer it. Could you steer it? If I put a rope on it? And towed it? Could you steer it? I could take her home and use her bits for my own wee motor. She's not in bad order."

I studied the wreck. Even if it was possible to find a piece of the junk-heap strong enough to hold a tow rope her "bits" would be scattered all over the field like the scaled dung before we ever made the hole in the hedge which gave access to the main road. Working on this assumption I decided to humour Dinger. I said I would do it.

That was my first introduction to the joys of motoring. Big mistake. For a start, Dinger didn't have a towrope. But as soon as he'd parted with his hard-earned fiver the hayseed farmer came up with a length of baling wire which he doubled up two or three times and tied to the front chassis of the henhouse. Dinger tied the other end to the back axle of his own vehicle.

The farmer scraped away the muck from the driver's seat with the back of his hand and wiped it tolerably clean with the remnant of a meal bag. He did the same with the steering wheel, which appeared to have been a particularly favourite place for the roosting hens. "In ye get," he cackled to me through half a mouthful of rotting yellow teeth. "Ye'll have her home in no time."

I shook my head and fell into the lately laundered seat. I peered through the glar on the windscreen, seeing practically nothing as Dinger powered his own Ford into life. I braced myself and watched the burst of blue smoke belch from the motor's exhaust and the remainder billow up through the holes in the floor and float around Dinger's head. Dinger, without giving me even so much as a nod, sunk his foot to the board and took off up the

———— ∞ ————

field in a cloud of flying turf and dung and grass and smoke like one of those American drag-racers.

I hadn't noticed what length of baling-wire the farmer had tied to the two motors. But Dinger was nearly out through the hole in the hedge leading on to the main road before the slack was taken up with such force and terrible rending and crashing noises I thought the henhouse had exploded around me. It hadn't. But suddenly we, that's the henhouse and myself, were hurtling across the field at a fierce rate of knots toward the hole in the hedge and the main road which I sincerely hoped would be clear of traffic – human, animal, mechanical, or otherwise. I was flung back hard in my seat and almost decapitated as the gee forces played havoc with my unprotected body. The steering wheel spun crazily and meaninglessly in my hands. The hayseed hadn't cleaned it as well as he might. My fingers slipped all over the squashed chicken droppings as I tried desperately to get some sort of grip. Just in time I gained a bit of control as we widened the hole in the hedge by about fifty per cent and tore out on to the road in pursuit of Dinger who was now disappearing around another corner and displaying not the slightest regard for my welfare or any other unfortunate who might be abroad on the Queen's highway.

I slammed my foot on the brake. It went straight to the floor and a little beyond that. I hit the light switch in an effort to send a message to Dinger that I was in no way in control of my vehicle and would he please slow down. On observing my headlights in his rear view mirror Dinger misinterpreted this signal as meaning I was reasonably happy with the performance of my vehicle thus far. He pressed his foot even harder down on the pedal and fairly tore round the next corner, narrowly avoiding taking an unplanned for journey through an adjacent plantation and almost wiping out some old dear in a pink bonnet who had innocently enough chosen that particular afternoon to go blackberrying.

This was crazy. It couldn't continue. I was going to be killed. I glanced down at the mucky gear stick, still clabbered with hen dung. I didn't want to do it. But it was my only chance. I took a deep breath. I slipped in the clutch, grabbed the dung-clabbered gear stick as firmly as I could and dropped it into top gear. I expected the henhouse to come to a sudden and grinding halt as engine, gearbox, drive shaft and every other movable part seized up. It didn't. I couldn't believe my ears, or my eyes either, as the engine bombed into life with an explosion that lifted the bonnet up a clean two feet in the air before it slammed down again to cover the smoking engine. I kicked desperately at the accelerator. It was jammed solid to the floor with the throttle wide open.

Suddenly we were within ten feet of Dinger and threatening to drive him clean off the road in about two point five seconds and at the same time set an all-time speed record for a motorised henhouse. I hit the brake again, kicked down the clutch and hauled desperately at the handbrake. Hopeless. I grabbed at the ignition key and tried to pull it out. It wouldn't move. That's when I abandoned every thought of survival, hoped my family would be well cared for and would remember me, covered my eyes and waited for peaceful oblivion.

When I opened my peepers I discovered the henhouse and I were situated comfortably in the middle of a whin bush, which up to that point had been growing serenely on the top of a grassy bank above the road and enjoying idyllic and uninterrupted views of Scrabo tower in the distance. Dinger was at the door of the henhouse, pulling it open and hauling me out.

"She goes!" he whooped excitedly. "She goes! I never even thought about tryin' to get her started! Well done! I thought you said you knew nothin' about motor cars!"

I leaned on the side of the henhouse, pulling in deep breaths of the dung-free fresh air and the sweet almond fragrance of the yellow flowered whins. I lifted my head and gazed thankfully upon the simple beauty of Scrabo Hill and the stately tower which surmounted it, sights I realised I had never given enough attention to in the past and sights I never expected to lay eyes upon again. I didn't think it was worth explaining to Dinger, whose enthusiasm for the henhouse was now totally unbounded that, far from attempting to get the henhouse to start, I had tried with all the limited skills at my disposal to achieve the very opposite.

"You know what this means," Dinger hooted excitedly. "You do know what this means!"

I shook my head. In a world that had suddenly gone completely nuts I no longer had any confirmed views as to what anything might mean.

"You can have the henhouse!" he exclaimed. "Gimmee six quid and it's yours! There's a ton of power in that wee engine. You nearly drove over the top of me. I'll help you to touch her up. A wee drop of Isopon and a lick of paint from Woollies and you'll be ready for the road! Experience the joys of motoring!"

We got the henhouse home to Dinger's backyard in the back deed. But not under its own steam. I insisted the ignition key be removed and retained in my pocket. If Dinger promised to tow the vehicle at a sensible speed I would attempt to steer it back to Newton. He agreed and I did.

I don't know if it was the shock of the adrenaline still pumping through my veins for the next two or three days. But I couldn't rid myself of the fact I had actually steered and driven a motor car on the open road all by myself - well, apart from the umbilical lump of baling wire which had secured my Ford to Dinger's Ford. Suddenly I began to see the wonderful possibilities motor car ownership opened up. No more bicycle. No more soakings on a wet morning. No more crowded buses. Go where you want. When you want. With whomever you want, though probably mostly with the wife and family. A life of freedom and excitement and discovery. Why had I not discovered the joys of motoring before this? Just like Dinger and the infamous Mr Toad, whom I had read about as a child, I was suddenly overcome and overwhelmed by the subtle charms of the combustion engine.

Yes. My first motor car was a henhouse. All winter Dinger and

I worked on my very own Ford 8. Every penny I earned went on making that wee motor truly fit for the road. Isopon, rust inhibitor, two second-hand tyres and a master cylinder. And the pièce de résistance, two tins of Woollies very best black gloss paint and a brand new paint brush to put it on with. When spring rolled around once more and the sweet scent of almond was again on the yellow whin bushes, my wee motor was ready. My acquisition of the henhouse, originally a Ford 8, and restored to as much of her former glory as would make her legally fit for the road, was the spur that started me off on a life-long love-hate relationship with the motor car.

But looking back over the years, motor cars have brought me nothing but trouble. Every single one I ever owned was a personal disaster for me. I think they're in a conspiracy against me. They're out to get me. For over forty years I've been the unfortunate owner of motor vehicles which refused point blank to start, nearly took the arm off me when I tried to get them going with a starting handle, wouldn't budge if the engine did take the notion to go, broke down miles from anywhere if they took it into their head to move, disappeared in a fit of instantaneous combustion and nearly finished me off out at the Six Road Ends when I finally capitulated to my wife's pleadings to "let her have a wee drive". But if you don't mind I'll stop here and fortify myself with a wee drop of something. Then I'll tell you of some of the terrible things that happened to me as I sought to experience the elusive joys of motoring and all brought about by my almost accidental acquisition of the Carrowdore henhouse.

The Joys of Motoring

I shouldn't have done it. Given in to my wife's pleadings, out at the Six Road Ends, to let her "have a wee drive." No way. I mean, she can't even steer a dodgem, let alone a full-blown motor vehicle. But she'd only just passed her driving test. To celebrate I was driving her and our two youngsters over to Donaghadee for a fish-supper in Ernie Giovannoli's and a bit of a dander round the lighthouse.

"Let me drive!" she insisted. "I know how to do it! I passed the driving test!" So, having enough of the bawling in my ear combined with the tried and tested gush of the waterworks and working on the assumption the fella who gave her the driving licence wouldn't have done it if he thought there was any real threat to life and limb, I considered her request. Immediately our little daughters in the back took to sobbing and pleading earnestly in my ear, "Don't do it Daddy! Don't let her drive!"

The youngsters' heartfelt sense of self preservation made an impact upon me as I recalled what happened when Teddie Tate took his life in his hands for two quid an hour and tried to teach the mother of my children to drive. Teddie, with my wife at the wheel, was bowling down Finlays Road at a fair rate of knots and closing fast on the Portaferry Road. For those not familiar with the geography and terrain of the area I will explain. At the end of Finlays Road you can turn left toward the delightful village of Greyabbey. Or turn right for the great wee town of Newtownards. The one thing you cannot do, with any degree of comfort, is proceed straight on. There are several reasons for this. I will mention just two, from which I think you will perceive the difficulties presented.

If you decide you have no particular desire to take the scenic route toward Greyabbey, nor turn right for the fair town of Newtownards, but continue in a straight line, you are met with a fairly insurmountable obstacle, namely a stone wall several feet in height. If you and your vehicle are fortunate enough, or unfortunate enough, to surmount this slight problem, you then become airborne for a period of time before making a not very aerodynamically efficient splash down in the waters of Strangford Lough. This does, however, immediately afford you fairly comprehensive close up and personal views of the Lough's marine life.

So, my wife and Teddie were roaring down this hill on the final few remaining yards of Finlays Road in Teddie's car into which he had sunk his life savings to fulfil a long held but not very wise desire to become self employed in the driving instructing business. Picture the scene. A balmy summer day. The Lough is full in, gleaming gold in the dazzling sun. Scrabo hill stands proud and beautiful and you can almost smell the purple heather growing on its many little hillocks. Seagulls wheel lazily in the clear blue sky and out on the Lough a few little boats, suspecting nothing, are drifting peacefully, completing the beautiful panorama. Teddie, a veteran of a dozen night-time raids over Berlin in a Lancaster, seemed not to be aware of the very real danger into which he had placed himself and was taking in the tranquillity of the scene before him.

However, abject terror and disbelief registered on his craggy face as my wife kept her foot hard down on the accelerator and sought to run out of road as quickly as she possibly could, displaying no particular desire to visit either Greyabbey or Newtownards, but showing a pretty definite resolve to join the sail boats in the Lough. As the wall and total oblivion came ever closer without causing a glimmer of interest in my wife, Teddie suddenly experienced an overwhelming desire to be once again strapped into the safety of a Lancaster bomber on a night mission over Berlin with only ack-ack guns and Messerschmitts to contend with. Teddie tried to speak – well actually he tried to scream – but nothing came out, and his white lips opened and closed like a fish stranded in a hayfield. Suddenly he recovered the use of his vocal chords, and his senses. "Mrs Robinson!" he screamed hysterically like a man in his death throes. "Mrs Robinson! We have neither sails nor oars! Hit the brakes! Now! NOW!"

Believing Teddie had called for an emergency stop, and who can lay any responsibility at her door for this as it is after all part of driving instruction, my wife obliged and powered as much of her twelve stone frame into the brake pedal as she could possibly manage. Tragedy was averted, apart from the slight inconvenience of Teddie going straight through the windscreen, which my wife declared was his own fault as he should have been ready for the stop since he was the one who asked for it. After extensive hospital treatment at no small expense to the already beleaguered National Health Service, Teddie retired forthwith from the driving instructing business and spent the rest of his days in a male commune on the isle of Iona which he reckoned was as far away from women and motor cars as he could possibly get. Every minute detail of this trivial incident flashed across my brain like lightning. Driving licence or no driving licence, I considered it might not be a wise decision to let my spouse lay hands upon the steering wheel of my wee Ford Eight into which I had invested many hard earned shekels and long hours of patching up. But she insisted, with a fair degree of entitlement, that she had the licence to prove she was legally entitled to drive on the County Road.

I do not know why. Looking back, I think it may have been some sort of death wish. I cannot say for certain. Anyway, I foolishly ignored the shrieks and pleadings coming from the children in the rear of the vehicle. I pulled over and let their mother take the controls of my motor car while the girls covered their eyes and threw themselves hysterically to the floor pleading to be let out of the vehicle or, failing that, for someone to immediately send for the police.

My wife did pretty well through the early gears and kept the vehicle between the hedges in more or less a straight line as she moved up to twenty miles per hour. Then she hit top and lost the plot completely. Suddenly we were tearing round the bends with a maximum of only two wheels touching the road at any one time. I made a desperate attempt for the ignition key and the youngsters were having convulsions as they bounced from one side of the car to the other and made an all out attempt to abandon the vehicle in mid journey.

Now we were heading down the hill toward the Six Road Ends with no indication yet that my dear wife intended to decrease the velocity of the vehicle to make an attempt on the right hand turn toward Donaghadee. This did not auger well for any of us. But it got worse. I quickly calculated, even in the middle of the mayhem going on around me, that we were driving on one of six roads due to meet at a junction in a very few number of seconds. If my arithmetic was correct, when we reached the junction there would be another five roads from which a vehicle of any description might innocently emerge and be wiped out before they even knew what hit them.

So, we're bombing down the hill, just a little below the speed at which I reckon we must soon, to comply with the laws of aerodynamics, become airborne. That's when I saw, emerging lazily from the Green Road, directly on our flight path, a wee Ford

Ferguson. Now I had nothing against wee grey Fergies. Indeed, I had a very great fondness for them. A Ford Ferguson was the first machine I ever drove, in Raymond Strain's spud field when I was only twelve years old. I held them in great affection ever since. I regret to say therefore that I was not greatly enamoured to see this particular Fergie crawl out from the Green Road, and even less than delighted to observe the ruckshifter and haystack it towed. As a youngster, I had spent many a happy hour in hayfields, turning the hay and building the ricks and riding on top of the haystack on the ruckshifter. Under normal circumstances I would have viewed the rustic scene before me with the greatest delight and pleasure. But these were not normal circumstances and, as I instantly recalled happy hours in the hayfields of bygone days, I was forcibly struck with the probability that this would be the last time I would make acquaintance with a ruck shifter and a haystack.

"Stop! Stop! STOP! Hit the brakes!" I bawled as the wee Fergie, ruckshifter and haystack, continued on into the road totally unaware of the disaster about to strike. "Stop NOW!" I roared, making one last plea for life and liberty as the Fergie, ruckshifter, and haystack came closer and closer. "We're going to be killed!"

"It is quite all right," declared my wife huffily and not batting an eyelid as she kept her foot to the board and headed straight for the hay. "It's okay. I have the right of the road!"

I have sound reason to believe the logic of the female of the species operates on a totally different basis to anything else in the known universe. My wife did have the right of the road. It could not be denied. But had she considered what might develop when an irresistible force such as this motor car met an unmovable object such as a wee grey Fergie not to mention ruckshifter and haystack? I did not think so. However, the road belonged to my wife.

Do not inquire of me how we survived. I do not know. We struck the shifter and haystack at a slightly reduced rate of knots as my wife suddenly realised having the right of the road could be a dangerous right if it was not mixed with a grain or two of common sense. Fortunately for us the ruckshifter was rather small and the haystack was rather large. My wee motor whaled into the haystack and threw it and the shifter on to its side and into the field from which they had lately come, taking the wee Fergie and its somewhat startled driver with it. We followed them into the field, motor, driver and passengers. The car doors burst open and we all landed, I suppose happily enough, in the remains of this haystack and I once again entertained sweet memories of days gone in a similar field under slightly different and more tranquil circumstances.

In years to come I experienced many more so-called joys of motoring. I will relate a few of them; titanic struggles between four wheeled vehicles and myself which, I seriously believed, were about to tip me into the realms of insanity.

We decided to go camping. Just my wife and myself. The children were now legally of an age whereby they could categorically refuse to risk life and limb by stepping inside any motor vehicle owned by myself. They exercised their legal right. So my wife and I prepared for a grand tour of England, Scotland and Wales. It would be good to get away for a bit of relaxation. Happy days.

Things began to go a little awry early on in this adventure. Very early on. I had just become the proud possessor of a sixteen-year-old Ford Cortina. She was in great order and with great expectations we loaded up. Tent, cooker, gas, sleeping bags, crockery, pillows, food box, suitcases, deck chairs, dining table, sun-tan lotion and every thing required for life on the open road. We sailed from Larne and were ready to get off the boat in Stranraer with no problem at all. Apart from the fact my Cortina was in pole position on the grid at the front of the boat and wouldn't start. Impatient engines revved behind us. Would-be Juan Fangios and Mike Hawthorns and Stirling Mosses were raring to be off to burn up the A74. Lights flashed in my rear view mirror, horns hooted, but I couldn't get my engine to give so much as a cough. I did get a "click". That's all. Just a click. Several clicks in fact. The big deckhand, whom I had observed for the past five minutes waving at me to drive off with one hand and tearing the remains of his somewhat sparse hair out with the other, came storming over. He poked his head through the open window.

"Yer starter's jammed," he bawled. "Give it a dunt!"

I thanked the man kindly for his information and advice and stared at him, none too much the wiser. "Where is it?" I asked politely.

"Where's what!" he roared in my ear.

"The starter," I replied civilly. "Where is it? So I can give it a dunt?"

I did not quite catch what the deckhand muttered under his breath, which is maybe just as well as I do not believe I could accurately record it here without giving offence and I am a great believer in giving the facts as they actually are and not as they might possibly have been.

"Open yer bonnet," he hollered. I pulled the clip and released the bonnet. My deckhand friend hauled it up and then strode over to the side of the deck and fumbled about in a toolbox. I have to admit to entertaining certain fears as to the future well being of my Cortina when I saw he carried toward us a very large hammer, which I perceived would come in extremely useful to anyone engaged in employment on a chain-gang. I sank down in my seat and pretended not to be there and my lady wife did likewise as the entertaining music and light show of horns, engines and glaring headlamps continued to perform behind us.

The big deckhand strode toward me with malice aforethought etched clearly on his not so handsome face. Suddenly my concern for the Cortina took a poor second place behind my very real anxiety for my own welfare. But at the last moment the deckhand altered course by a few degrees. I breathed a sigh of relief as he headed for the open bonnet.

The big man swung back the hammer and fairly laid into the engine of my Ford Cortina which immediately suggested to me that whatever its earlier chances of leaving the boat, they were now considerably reduced. I shuddered and grimaced as I listened three times to the horrific crack of steel upon steel. Then the bonnet was slammed down and the big man's face was in the window beside me again.

"Try her now!" he glowered. I did. The engine roared into life immediately. I rammed her into gear and nearly burned the clutch out as we shot off the boat and down the ramp, giving a final wave of grateful thanks to my friend with the magic hammer. Interesting, I mused, as we cleared the dock. Very interesting. I'd had plenty of motors that wouldn't start. But it never entered my noggin to take a sledge-hammer and lay into them and let them know just who's boss. I filed that away for future reference as we set off on the road and the miles to Dumfries and to sometimes sunny but usually rainy Blackpool.

Blackpool was fine. Well – Blackpool was Blackpool. Cheap and cheerful and okay for a bit of a laugh. But it was only an overnight stop on our grand tour that would take in the beauty of Shakespeare's Stratford-upon-Avon, the Lake District, the South coast, beautiful Devon and the mysterious land that is Cornwall. Well, that was the idea.

But, as the old adage says, 'the best laid plans o' mice and men aft gang astray', to which I can well testify. It has often been my experience that my plans aft gang astray, especially when motor cars play any sort of part in them. Such was the case with the grand tour. We had the usual day out in sunny Blackpool without the sun – losing a packet on the slot-machines, getting ripped off at mock auctions and over-eating on fish and chips. A great day. Then we decided to head back up to the campsite.

The car was in the park at the back of the Golden Mile. Well, it was when I last saw it. It wasn't now. No problem. Obviously I had parked it somewhere else. I tried a different place in the car park where I thought I might have left the trusty machine. Nothing.

Maybe I left it in another car park? Oh yes? Maybe I didn't bring the car? Maybe we walked in from the campsite? Uh-huh - the whole six miles? Maybe I'm looking for the wrong car. Maybe I'm on Candid Camera. Maybe I'm dreaming. Dream on, baby. This was no dream.

Finally the message got through. Our car had been stolen and what are we going to do six miles away from the campsite with no way to get there and no way to move the tent and half a ton of camping gear when we do.

Tell the police. Good thinking. The police station was a big skyscraper overlooking the car park. It bristled with all sorts of aerials and antennas and CCTV cameras. They must have seen the attempt on my car. Probably beetled across the street and apprehended the criminals in the act and had my Ford in their compound for safe keeping until I got there to claim it.

Some hope. Gaining access to the police station was maybe just a shade more difficult than walking in to the Belfast branch of the Northern Bank to knock off a couple of million smackers. But I was in no mood to be denied. Eventually I gained entry. After waiting for about thirty minutes to state the nature of my business I was informed the Blackpool police force knew nothing about a goldie coloured Ford Cortina with a funny number plate. I advised them there was nothing funny about the number plate in the part of the U.K. I came from and in no way did I see the theft of my vehicle in any way a laughing matter. I expected the Blackpool police force to immediately put out an all points bulletin with road blocks on every route out of town in an all out effort to intercept the desperados and return my vehicle to me within the hour.

I was disappointed. I was told to "join the queue." When I enquired as to which queue I was being invited to join as the interior of Blackpool police station had enough queues to put the entire Soviet Union to shame, I was told with a wave of the hand "That one. The one for stolen vehicles." I quickly came to the realisation the queue for stolen vehicles was already twenty persons long. The man in front of me was lamenting to the lady in front of him about the loss of his two day old silver Mercedes. I began to realise Blackpool police force might be somewhat reticent about putting out an all points bulletin in an effort to retrieve my sixteen year old Cortina with the funny number plate.

The situation took a decided turn for the worse when I finally got to the head of the queue. I was informed, in certain words which left no room for misunderstanding, it was extremely unlikely I would ever see my Ford Cortina with the funny number plate again as by this time it would be in Sheffield or Rotherham and already broken down for parts. If I desired to waste my own time and that of the Blackpool police force I could fill up a form declaring the theft. If some dark night the police should happen to stumble upon the Cortina they would inform me in due course.

I staggered from the police station in a state of utter shock. Finally, when Blackpool closed down for the night, which wasn't night, but the early hours of the morning, we hailed a taxi to the campsite. The grand tour of mainland U.K. had shuddered to a complete and total halt. We were stuck in a field six miles from anywhere with a tent and enough gear to accommodate the British army on an overseas tour of duty for six months. But, as the old adage says, 'things look better in the morning'.

"Let us take a stroll into Blackpool," I suggested to my wife after a fairy miserable breakfast, "and have another look for the motor car. Some day we will look back on all this and laugh."

My wife declared it would be unlikely she would live to see that particular day but nevertheless agreed to accompany me on the hike back to town. We set off to tramp the six miles to the town of fun and laughter and search again for the missing car. Here I must point out that occasionally, very occasionally, Miss Lady Luck does indeed take it upon herself to shine on me. This morning she choose to do that very thing. We were well within sight of the illustrious Tower where on many occasions I had ballroom danced and entertained the hope that in happier times I might do so again. Suddenly, set back in the driveway of a fairly posh manor I spied this magnificent looking automobile with a lump of cardboard stuck on the windscreen informing all citizens who passed by that the vehicle was for sale at the giveaway price of only £800.

Eight hundred smackers was just about ten times the ceiling I had ever shelled out for any automobile. Indeed, I once purchased a wee black Morris Minor with cardboard mudguards for only nine pounds and ten shillings, which in today's parlance is nine pounds and fifty pence. But that is another story and another disaster and I do not have time nor space to detail it here. But there is always another book.

Anyway, I gazed upon this thing of great beauty sitting in this gent's driveway. I recalled the old adage 'seek and ye shall find' and I began to think it was no accident this motor had suddenly been revealed to me. I immediately formulated certain plans which I considered might deliver us from the unfortunate dilemma into which we were well and truly sunk at that time.

I invited my wife to rest her aching pins while I took a closer look at the shiny motor, which was a Peugeot 505 and not by any means a banger. The gleaming gold paintwork was perfection itself. So was the immaculate interior. I dived underneath. Finding no indication of holes in the floor, Isopon or exhaust bandages, I knocked upon the door of the manor and engaged the owner of the vehicle in conversation. He gave such a thrilling and complete history of the motor, including the fact it had only been on the road twice since new and was serviced every other week by the best garage in town and was a genuine snip at only the eight hundred sheets of green, I was impressed. But why, I asked, was the gentleman selling such a superb vehicle, the like of which he had assured me was not to be found between here and Lands End, and I had no reason to disagree with him, for the silly price of eight hundred quid? Well, he informed me, he was the owner of a large chain of very financially secure betting shops that were placed in every city, town, village and hamlet in the land. But he had grown weary of the rat race and the consumer society and everything that money could buy. He hinted it had not brought him the happiness he thought it might. So he was departing Blackpool's fair shores the next morning to commence life as a Buddhist monk in a remote village on the fringes of the Tibetan mountains. He very much doubted he would require his beautiful Peugeot 505, though it was breaking his tender heart in two that he must soon be parted from it. I began to wonder if the gentleman was so set on a life of penury and self abasement that maybe if I asked him nicely he might let me drive his Peugeot away for free. That would save him any further heartbreak or risk of contamination by the insertion of filthy lucre into his wallet, not to mention loss of time in getting to the mountains of Tibet. Or, at the very least, would he be willing to lower the asking price, especially if I appraised him of the desperate situation in which my wife and I found ourselves?

The gentleman informed me he could wish for no better person than myself to take ownership of the joy of his heart. But sadly no. He had given away all his worldly wealth. He must hold out for possession of the full eight hundred as that was the sum of money required to take him to his Tibetan destination where he could be free evermore from filthy lucre and the baubles and bangles it might purchase. And he needed the dough today.

For me this was a problem. A big problem. I did not have eight hundred sheets with me. But I had exactly that amount sitting safely in my bank account back home where I hoped it would have a safe and happy lodging until such times, as the old adage says, a rainy day might come along. Although the sun was shining brightly I convinced myself this was one of the rainiest days I had seen for some considerable time. I took steps to immediately remove my eight hundred from the secure vaults back home and deliver it into the hands of the soon to be Tibetan monk. The old adage 'a fool and his money are soon parted' popped into my head. I ignored it. Very shortly the eight hundred was no longer mine but the property of the dear soul who was about to unchain himself from the curse of money and all it could buy.

By late afternoon my wife and I were the proud owners of the gleaming Peugeot 505. We cruised triumphantly toward the campsite after having spent a wonderful day in the fun-filled town of Blackpool, which included a visit to see Mr Ken Dodd and his happiness show at the Opera House.

Everything went splendidly on the road to the campsite. The purr of the engine, the electric windows, the stereo system, and the plush upholstery. What a motor car! I drove to a leisurely halt at a set of traffic lights, just before the old windmill at Marton Mere.

The lights turned amber. Then green. I accelerated away in first gear. The trouble commenced when I went looking for the second of the gears in the five-speed box. The gear stick came away in my hand. Right up from the floor it came, and I was left gazing at it in wonderment while the vehicle, now in no gear whatsoever, slowed to a crawl and drivers all around me took evasive action and hooted their horns and flashed their lights in such a frenzy I believed they might well have been the same crowd who gave me a rough time when departing the boat at Stranraer. However, I steered the stricken Peugeot into a lay-by with one hand and held on tightly to the useless gear stick with the other.

I switched off the engine. I was in shock. I gazed down the long winding road along which we were no longer travelling, toward the campsite. I stared down at the gear stick in my hand. I reflected upon my now empty bank account back home. The old adage about the fool and his money floated mockingly across my numbed mind. But I would not be defeated. I threw the gear stick to the floor and in a muddled daze walked over to the pub across the way and phoned the R.A.C. The R.A.C. asked me where I was and I told them I was in the pub. They said which pub. I found out and told them the name of the pub. They asked me in which part of the world was this particular pub, which I told them when I found out myself and the R.A.C. man showed up.

I was relieved to find that a Peugeot without a gear stick presented no big problem for him. "I'll go first," he explained, opening the door of his own vehicle. "Follow me to our own garage. I'll have you back on the road in no time."

"How can I follow you," I asked. "I haven't got a gear stick!"

The R.A.C. man scratched his head. "Mmmm. Forgot about that." He fumbled about in his toolbox. He produced a large screwdriver and a hammer not unlike the one the deckhand used with great success on my Cortina at Stranraer and which impressed upon me even more strongly the necessity of acquiring one of those useful implements as soon as possible. He handed the tools to me. "Stick that screwdriver in the hole where the gear lever was" he instructed me. "And hit it a good crack with the hammer. Then follow me."

I did as I was told. Clobbering motor cars with sledgehammers seemed a pretty effective method of repairing ailing four wheeled machines. I made a mental note to purchase one at my earliest convenience. The screwdriver in the gearbox proved so successful I reckoned we could complete the grand tour without the need of a gear stick. But the R.A.C. man said no, let's fix it properly, which he eventually did, and I cannot speak too highly of the skills of the aforesaid R.A.C. man whose name I forgot to enquire.

But all this business with the jammed starter, the pinched Ford and the removable gear lever somewhat rattled our confidence and ambition to complete the grand tour. We decided to settle for two weeks in sometimes sunny Blackpool. Next year we would tackle the grand tour in the comfort of the big Peugeot 505 after it had been fully road tested on a flat out run down the Ards peninsula to Portaferry and back.

The Peugeot never saw Portaferry. It was midnight when we arrived home after our holiday. We weren't going to unload the car at this hour. We tumbled straight into bed. I was out like a light and dreaming of Cortinas and car parks and jammed starters and broken gear levers and all things mechanical when I heard a violent hammering. I thought I was driving down the M6 and a piston had just come up through the bonnet and I was wondering what to do next when the hammering came again, even louder than before. Suddenly I awoke and realised I was safe in my own little bed. So what was the hammering? Finally it dawned upon me. Someone is at the front door.

I glanced at the clock. Six thirty a.m. I dragged myself down stairs and opened the door. There stood a hearty member of the Royal Ulster Constabulary.

"Good mornin', sir," grunted the officer. "Are you the owner of a gold Peugeot 505 registration number YES 2013?"

I blinked, trying to take in the information supplied to me and fumbling in my mind to come up with the right answer.

"Yes," I finally sighed sleepily. "Why?"

"Where is the vehicle now, sir?" enquired the officer.

I pointed wearily toward the street. "Out there. At the front door."

The policeman shook his head. "I am afraid not. It is lyin' half way through a hedge in a spud field outside Millisle. You were not aware it had been stolen?"

That did it for me. The long-lasting love affair with motor cars ended right there and then. On my doorstep. I'd had enough. I quit. I didn't know where the Peugeot ended up and much less did I care. I hauled our bits and pieces from it and asked the police to tow it to the scrap yard of their choice. With pleasure I would pay the bill.

I am back to riding the pushbike. Have been for some time. My worst experience on two wheels was a puncture. But I'm not getting any younger and the hills are getting steeper and my legs don't have the power they used to. And they say motor cars are more reliable now. Don't break down as often. Don't rust. You never need to replace the battery. And they're harder to steal. I was looking at a beauty the other day in that big showroom

Witness for the Prosecution

It was the parrot's fault. Well, maybe not all the blame can be laid at the feet, or more precisely, the beak of the parrot. Clancy has to carry his own share of responsibility for what happened. Anybody who'd go to a court of law over a missing bag of coal and put a parrot on the stand as the main witness for the prosecution couldn't, in all conscience, blame the bird if it refused to testify on the day. So maybe it wasn't all the parrot's fault.

Oul' Clancy McCrory was a bit of a recluse. In fact, more than a bit. He was a one hundred percent dyed in the wool recluse, or, as the whole of the Ards peninsula reckoned, a total nutcase. I wouldn't necessarily agree that Clancy was a prime candidate for the loony bin. I'd worked with him in the Regent factory, before both of the disasters happened to him. But there was no doubt, even then, that he was two or three rounds short of a loaf of bread.

Clancy dwelled on the pleasant banks of Strangford Lough between Greyabbey and Kirkcubbin in a wee tumble down cottage with a half-door that was never open, summer or winter. Once upon a time the cottage's whitewashed walls had gleamed brightly in the summer sun that flecked the lough. The little windows and half-door were always given a coat of shiny new paint every year, green one season and red the next. It was as nice a wee cottage as an American tourist would want to lay eyes on and Clancy kept it as spick and span inside as he did out. Of course he was all right in those days, before it happened. The cottage was to be a comfortable and happy abode for himself and the love of his life, the pretty faced Liza Jane McCormack with whom Clancy had been keeping company for a number of years and hoped soon to make his wife.

But all that was a long time ago when Clancy was still a relatively young and sensible man, if you can call forty nine young, and before Liza Jane stood him up at the altar and he lost his marbles. Folk say that's what tipped Clancy over the edge. That's when the strangeness first came upon him. Clancy walked home alone from the church on the day he didn't get married. He shut himself away in his wee cottage. He never returned to the Regent Factory and from that day on bothered with no one if he could possibly avoid it. On the odd occasion he met anyone on the road if he was out for a bit of a dander, he'd dive into a slap in the hedge and conceal himself until they'd passed by. The youngsters threw stones at the roof of his cottage as they strolled home from school and usually achieved their aim of getting a good hunt from Clancy with the added bonus that he would break their necks if he were ever fortunate enough to lay hands upon them.

Clancy lived his later years alone in the wee cottage, speaking to no one and trusting no one. On winter nights he'd light a miserable fire and a candle and read books about how the world began and books about how the world would end. In summer he laboured the wee bit of ground at the side of the cottage that caught the all day sun shining above the lough. That gave him something to do and with the two or three chickens he reared, kept him in food for most of the year. He rarely visited a shop.

The bread server was obliged to leave the soda and wheaten every Tuesday and Friday in the white enamelled breadbin Clancy left at the end of the lonen with the correct money inside. A similar arrangement was set up for the milkman. The only outsider who ever had occasion to come down the lonen was the coalman. Clancy no longer had the strength of body to carry the coal in the wheelbarrow the length of the rough path to his cottage. But the old man still left the money for the coal in a tin box just inside the coalhouse to save himself the trouble of having to greet the coalman. For Clancy, it was a harsh and lonely life.

Until the parrot arrived. From nowhere. Clancy dragged himself from bed as usual one cool autumn morning and peered through the window straight across the lough to Scrabo to get a sense of what sort of day it might be. And there was the green parrot with the yellow head. Perched right in the laurel bush just outside the cottage window. Clancy gazed at the parrot. The parrot, suddenly catching Clancy's movements from inside the window, cocked its head, muttered something, and stared straight back. Clancy expected the bird to fly away once it saw him. It didn't.

Clancy pulled on a few rags and shuffled to the door. He turned the keys in the two locks and removed the iron bar he always dropped between the doorposts each night before he retired, though no one at any time had tried to force an entry to his property. He pulled open the top half of the door and leaned his arms on the bottom half, gazing at the parrot. The parrot gazed right back. It ruffled its feathers, hammered its beak on the solid branch of the laurel bush and then squawked "Hello. It's a nice day!"

Clancy gazed across the grey misty lough to where Scrabo Tower was barely visible through dark threatening clouds. He'd seen nicer days. But never a parrot that could talk. Clancy was immediately taken by the bedraggled and wet bird perched in the laurel bush. He dragged open the lower half of the door and shuffled out toward the bird who paid him no particular attention but continued to inform him, despite all evidence to the contrary, that it was a nice day.

The parrot shifted from one leg to the other on its perch and uttered a low guttural sound as Clancy reached over and cautiously lifted it from the bush. "Hokey flute!" it squawked loudly. "Hokey flute! Here's a business! Here's a business!"

But the parrot immediately took to Clancy just as much as Clancy took to the parrot and made no fuss at all as the old man carried it into the house and set it on the table and offered it a bit of soda bread. The parrot appeared to have a liking for soda bread, and wheaten too, and as Clancy discovered, was very partial to an apple but couldn't have cared less about cheddar cheese or any other sort of cheese. As he fed the parrot Clancy peered at the ring on the bird's left leg and the numbers engraved upon it. The numbers meant nothing to Clancy and probably even less to the parrot.

With every day that passed Clancy waited for someone to knock upon his door and claim the parrot. Nobody ever did. So Clancy continued to give it a home and fed it and watered it and, because it was green in colour - almost fluorescent green, he named the bird Paddy, and that came to be the name the parrot responded to. The parrot was indeed a talker. A real talker. He never shut his mouth, from morning til night. Clancy didn't mind. Now of a winter evening he had a bit of company by the fireside. He yarned away to the parrot about his troubles and woes and the cares of life in general and expounded his beliefs and theories on all mankind and its selfishness until the bird almost knew what the old man was thinking and very often answered him back with the precise words Clancy wanted to hear to confirm his theories.

With the passing of time Paddy, having nothing to do all day and all night but listen to Clancy give out about how he saw the world and the people in it, the parrot came to be a superb conversationalist in his own right. And not only a conversationalist. The bird started to think for itself. At least that's the way it appeared, as Paddy began to share with Clancy his own philosophy on life. As the bird's only sounding board was Clancy himself, the two agreed on almost everything except the weather, which for Paddy continued to be a very nice day no matter what was happening outside.

Then Clancy taught the parrot to count. He started off by holding up a finger and repeating "one" over and over again. When Paddy finally got to grips with "one" Clancy held up two fingers and taught Paddy the significance and difference between two fingers and one finger. It took many, many months, but eventually Paddy could rhyme off one to twelve with no bother at all. He got stuck at thirteen. He could not get to grips with thirteen, or any teen, but fluttered about in his cage in annoyance and frustration while croaking over and over again "Hokey flute! Here's a business! Here's a business."

But Clancy was delighted with Paddy's numerical skills, basic as they were. He decided to take the bird a stage further and see how it would perform in the realms of practical arithmetic. Clancy took to setting the parrot's cage in the window so he could see Tobias Totten's lorry drive up the lonen to deliver the coal. Clancy taught the bird to count the bags as Tobias unloaded the coal and carried them past the window to the outhouse where he emptied them for Clancy's convenience.

"Coalman, one bag full," he taught the parrot, holding up one finger as Tobias struggled past the window with the first heavy bag on his shoulders. Then, as the coalman carried in the second bag Clancy pointed, held up two fingers, and informed the parrot "Coalman, two bags full" and so on until the parrot was able to enumerate exactly the number of bags of coal Tobias delivered on each journey, provided he never got to number thirteen which he never did.

Clancy and Paddy dwelled together in perfect harmony. They chatted away to one another all the day long and for a bit of a change counted coal bags every time Tobias called. It came to pass that on a certain day when Tobias was to deliver coal to the wee cottage Clancy had an unavoidable appointment in Newtownards. Clancy hated having to leave the comfort, security and seclusion of his little home. Even more did he detest having to go up to the town and of necessity be amongst a crowd of people whom he didn't even know. Worse than that, the day he was forced to be absent from the cottage was the very day on which Tobias would make a delivery of coal.

This greatly troubled Clancy. Since he'd been left standing alone at the altar all those years ago he'd never trusted another soul. And especially not Tobias Totten. The old man wasn't ignorant of Tobias's reputation for accidentally spilling a shovelful of coal from every bag he unloaded on to the floor of his lorry. Of a dozen or so bags to be delivered, thanks to the spilled coal, Tobias usually only parted company with maybe eleven bags. Clancy's eagle eye ensured it never happened to him. He was never short changed. But who could tell what might happen when he was up in Newtownards and Tobias was left to his own devices with nobody to keep an eye on him? Nobody to watch for spillage, or maybe worse, the short delivery of a whole bag? Clancy had nearly half a ton of coal piled up in the outhouse for the winter. It wouldn't be easy to tell if crafty Tobias took advantage of the situation and left him a bag short. Clancy was perplexed.

Then he remembered the parrot. The parrot could sit in the window and count the bags. "Coalman one bag full. Coalman two bags full," and so on. He'd done it plenty of times. Without a hitch. When Clancy came home he'd simply say to the parrot, "Coalman, bags?" and Paddy would tell him how many bags Tobias had emptied. He didn't really think Tobias would deliberately under deliver him. But you couldn't trust anybody. It was better to leave nothing to chance. And if Tobias did get up to his dirty tricks, Paddy would know about it. And if Paddy knew about it, so would Clancy.

On the day Clancy was to ride the bicycle up to Newtownards and Tobias was to deliver the coal, Clancy positioned Paddy in pole position in the window. He pulled the curtains well back to give the bird the best of all possible views. He pointed outside. "Coalman come, Paddy" he instructed the parrot as the bird cocked his head and stared at him. "Coalman come," repeated Clancy. "How many bags? One bag full. Two bags full. Three bags full. Four bags full," said Clancy with special emphasis on the word four which was the magic number Tobias would have to deliver to satisfy Paddy's numerological skills and observance of fair play. Clancy held up four fingers in front of the parrot's eyes. "Four bags full, Paddy" he repeated "Four bags full."

Clancy pulled his ramshackle bicycle from the coal shed and set out for Newtownards with Paddy happily ensconced in the window waiting for Tobias and the magic number of coal bags. When he reached the floodgates on the edge of Newton Clancy spied Tobias's coal lorry coming toward him from the other direction. Grudgingly Clancy exchanged token waves with Tobias, which was probably the most contact they'd had with each other in over a year. Clancy wasn't exactly thrilled and delighted to see Tobias head toward his un-attended home. Conversely Tobias, for whatever reason, was not displeased to see Clancy travelling away from it.

It took Clancy a good two hours to complete his business in Newton after which he threw his leg over the bicycle and pedalled as hard as he could back down the Portaferry Road and home. When he arrived he immediately dismounted from the bike and pulled open the coalhouse door. Tobias had made a delivery. No doubt about that. But how much had he delivered? Clancy couldn't tell. But he had a feeling things were not just as they should be. He dumped the bicycle into the coal shed to protect it from the steady rain, which had just begun to fall. He unlocked the back door of the cottage and pushed his way in to speak with the only one in the world he could trust, his good friend, the tried, the trusted, Paddy.

"Hello, Paddy boy," he greeted the dozing bird as if nothing was amiss. "Coalman come. How many bags?"

Paddy jumped about on his perch and ruffled his feathers in

———— ∞ ————

response to the rude awakening. He said nothing. "Coalman come," repeated Clancy pointing through the window. "How many bags?"

"Coalman come," answered Paddy still hopping about on his perch "Coalman come. Three bags. Three bags full."

Clancy frowned, a deep worried frown. "Paddy," he entreated the bird again, pointing outside. "Coalman come. How many bags?"

Paddy took once more to hopping excitedly about his perch. He appeared decidedly unhappy at being repeatedly questioned on a matter to which he had already given a clear and unequivocal answer. "Coal man come!" he squawked angrily. "Three bags! Three bags full! Hokey flute. Here's a business. Here's a business!"

Clancy drew his chair up beside the parrot. He took off his cap and interrogated the bird over and over again as to how many bags of coal Tobias had delivered. The parrot never deviated once from his original answer. "Coal man come!" he screeched. "Three bags! Three bags full! Hokey Flute! Here's a business!"

At ten past six in the evening Clancy still could not get Paddy beyond three bags of coal. The bird would not be moved in any way to change its answer to the question. Livid with rage, Clancy was finally convinced Tobias had conned him, just as he'd known he would once the opportunity presented itself so easily as it had. But if Tobias thought Clancy McCrory was going to stand by and be made a sucker of – well, he had another think coming. This was far and away the worst thing that had happened to him since Liza Jane had left him standing at the altar. But this time he wouldn't be made a fool of. No sir. He'd get justice. One way or another, he'd get what belonged to him. In cash or in kind.

Despite the fact he hadn't eaten a morsel of food since his porridge breakfast, Clancy hauled the bicycle back out from the coal shed. He pulled on his greatcoat to help turn the heavy rain which now lashed down. He slammed his peak cap on top of his grey head and with a final instruction to the parrot to mind the house

Clancy set out to pedal the whole way back to Newtownards. And the home of Tobias Totten.

The bitter wind and stinging rain sleeted down, cutting harshly into Clancy's face as he struggled along the exposed Portaferry Road. The old man fumed inwardly and cursed aloud as the wind howled from off the lough and made it almost impossible for him to turn the pedals. It was a long haul to Newtownards. Every inch of the journey gave Clancy more and more time to dwell upon the injustice that had been done to him. He was in no mood for explanation of any sort when totally exhausted and dripping wet with rain he finally hurled his bicycle against the wall of Tobias's house and thumped angrily on the door.

It was Tobias, a tall well-proportioned man, who opened the door. Clancy felt the comforting heat of the house meet him from the hallway and waft over him as Tobias stood before him in crimson carpet slippers and matching dressing gown, so neatly turned out Clancy barely recognised him.

"Tobias," barked Clancy, keeping his words to a minimum as his voice shook with emotion. "I paid you to leave me four bags of coal!"

Tobias stared with slight annoyance at the shapeless, soaking wet figure in front of him. He didn't like to be pulled away from his warm fireside. Especially on a night like this.

"That's right," he agreed. "Four bags. That's what you paid for. That's what I left."

"You left three!" snapped Clancy holding three fingers up directly under Tobias's nose. "Three bags. Not four. Don't think you're goin' to pull the wool over my eyes!"

Despite his physical superiority Tobias took a half step further back into the safety of his hallway as he saw Clancy's rain soaked face contort with rage. He thought the old man was going to lash out and strike him. But Tobias stood his ground and even regained the half step he had retreated towards the safety of his blazing fireside. His own temper flared in response to the charge hurled against him.

"Hold on just one minute, Clancy McCrory! Are you accusin' me of short-deliverin' your coal?"

"That's exactly what I'm accusin' you of," bellowed Clancy. "Four bags I paid you for. You took the money. But you knew I wasn't at home so you only left three bags!"

"Who says I only left three?" demanded Tobias. "You weren't there!"

"You're dead right I wasn't there! And you knew it. But Paddy was there!"

"Who's Paddy – when he's at home?" mocked Tobias, knowing full well Clancy lived alone and wouldn't let another soul cross his threshold.

"Paddy the parrot," declared Clancy defiantly. "My parrot! He can count, every bit as well as you can. I knew you'd be up to yer oul' tricks when you knew I wasn't home. But Paddy was there. Sittin' in the window. Watchin' you bringin' in the bags. Aye, and countin' them as well. And he says you only delivered three bags!"

"A parrot!" echoed Tobias in disbelief. "A parrot! That talks? And counts bags of coal! Are ye right in the head Clancy! Get away from my doorstep before I call the peelers and get you locked you up!"

Tobias's generous offer to arrange for Clancy to spend the rest of the evening in the comparative warmth and comfort of the barracks in Conway Square only served to make the old recluse even more mad than he was before. Tobias was again forced to retreat back into the relative safety of his hallway as Clancy came after him and poked him hard in the chest.

"Don't you talk to me about peelers!" raged Clancy. "I'll be the one that'll be gettin' the peelers! You're a daylight robber, Tobias Totten! And everybody knows it! Give me the money for my bag of coal or I'll be seein' ye in court!"

"In court!" sneered the coalman. "And your only witness a stupid bird who thinks he can count. You'll be gettin' no money from me, Clancy McCrory. Away ye go home and put your parrot over his sums again! And get yourself a new coalman!"

Clancy opened his mouth to further lay into Tobias and inform him he most certainly would be seeking a new coalman because when he, Clancy, had finished with him, Tobias would be in the clink and out of business. But Tobias slammed the door so abruptly and savagely in his face the brass knocker danced up and down several times and didn't afford Clancy time to pass on these sentiments.

Clancy boiled with rage as he stared at the closed door. He raised his boot with the intention of kicking it right through the obstacle that separated him from his now avowed enemy. Somehow, he restrained himself. But his face was white with fury and his entire body shook violently as he grabbed hold of his bicycle from where it leaned against the wall. He gripped the handlebars tightly and set his foot on the pedal. If he had to go to law to get justice, to law Clancy McCrory would go.

∞

Clancy could not believe how difficult it was to go to law. His solicitor wouldn't take the case. There wasn't a solicitor in the whole of Newtownards who would take the case. Every one of them did exactly the same thing. Smiled condescendingly and advised him, free of charge, to forget all about the matter and get himself a new coalman. But Clancy would not, could not, forget all about the matter. And he did not want a new coalman. From now on if he needed a fire he would buy a bag of turf from the corner shop in Greyabbey and wheel it home on the bar of his bike. It would be hard work. But he'd know he'd got what he paid for.

Despite the advice given him, Clancy was remorseless in his search for justice and recompense for the wrong he believed had been done to him. Every day he hammered on the door of the police barracks to seek what meagre advice he could from the amused officers. The persistence paid off. The day came when Clancy finally managed to make good his threat to observe Tobias in a court of law. But he had to prosecute the case himself.

On the day justice was to be done and seen to be done, Clancy rose early. He pulled on his best suit, which coincidentally also happened to be his only suit, and travelled up to Newtownards by bus. He begrudged paying the fare. But it had to be done. Anyway, it would be worth twice the price to put Tobias behind bars where he belonged. Paddy sat in his cage on the seat beside him. The bird said nothing. Clancy had taken the precaution of putting a cloth over the parrot's cage to keep him quiet. He didn't think the bird had been on a bus before, unless that was how he had travelled down to Clancy's cottage in the first place. But that was unlikely and Clancy didn't want the bird to get excited. This would be a big day for the parrot. It would be a big day for both of them.

Clancy's efforts to have his day in court took a turn for the worse before he even got into the courthouse. They wouldn't let him in.

"What's that under your arm?" demanded the hefty security man as he poked a finger at Paddy's cage and tried to pull the cover off.

"That's Paddy," declared Clancy, none too pleased to be halted this early in his search for justice.

"Paddy?" queried the security man. "Paddy who?"

"Paddy the parrot," spat Clancy. "I'm takin' him in to court with me."

"Oh no you're not," growled the security man. "You're not takin' a parrot in there. It's against the law."

Clancy almost had his day in court much quicker than he imagined he would as he remonstrated loudly with the man in charge of security. Two police officers were called to separate them as Clancy tried to impress upon the man that his parrot was a very important witness in the case of the missing bag of coal in which he himself was to take part. The security man straightened his tie and sniffed. He looked oddly at Clancy and bade him wait where he was with his budgie while he took advice on the matter. When he returned he informed Clancy that he was quite correct in stating that under no circumstances were animals or birds of any sort allowed within the court. But as the Clerk of the Court had already got wind that this bird was part of the case to come, an exception would be made. But neither Clancy nor the parrot would be permitted to enter the courtroom until the case was called and even then only on condition the bird would speak only when spoken to.

Newtownards courthouse was full to overflowing and a disgruntled crowd who had failed to gain admittance were attempting to storm the doors outside. Attending court cases was a marvellous source of free and most enjoyable entertainment for many Ards folk. It passed the day very pleasantly to observe people you knew get their comeuppance for riding their bike without a bell or maybe being involved in a fracas, "drink being taken". The *Chronicle* and *Spectator* newspapers reported the dastardly deeds and those guilty of them in their columns on a weekly basis, thereby extending the shame and entertainment value for another week or two. But today excitement was at fever pitch. For weeks the entire town and the whole peninsula had talked of nothing but Clancy's vendetta against Tobias and the case of the supposedly missing bag of coal.

The case was called within the hour which was just as well as Paddy was beginning to get a bit restless. He fluttered about underneath the cloth but to his credit remained silent and didn't even make a comment upon weather conditions outside. The court was informed of Clancy's charge against his former coalman. Clancy was called to take the stand, take the oath, and give such evidence as he had to support his accusation.

"If, as I understand it, Mr McCrory," said the Magistrate at the outset of the hearing "you were on business in the town of Newtownards on the day when these bags of coal were delivered,

———— ∞ ————

or not delivered, as the case may be, what evidence do you have to support your claim they were in fact under delivered?"

"Because Paddy told me," declared Clancy triumphantly. "That's how I know!"

The Magistrate looked over the top of his reading glasses. He peered at Clancy. "Paddy? Who, pray, is Paddy?"

"Paddy is my parrot," enthused Clancy, as he pointed to the cloth-covered cage beside him. "Paddy was sittin' in the window when the coal was delivered. He counted the bags. Only three of them. You can ask him."

The Magistrate looked hard at the Clerk of the Court who shrugged as if to absolve himself of all responsibility. He addressed Clancy once more. "Am I to understand, Mr McCrory, that the main witness for the prosecution in this case is a – a parrot? That you wish this - this court to accept the evidence of a – a bird?"

"Not just an ordinary bird, your honour, m'lord," declared Clancy as sniggers of amusement rippled across the courtroom. "Paddy can talk. An' count. He's a great counter. He can go up to twelve. I teached him myself."

The Magistrate glared once more at the unfortunate Clerk of the Court who shuffled some papers nervously and commenced to study his fingernails. The Magistrate lowered his head and rubbed his brow in disbelief. "Reveal unto us then, Mr McCrory, if you will, this talking, counting parrot."

Another series of giggles flitted across the courtroom as Clancy dramatically swept the cloth from Paddy's cage and let it fall to the floor revealing to the Magistrate and the court a somewhat confused Paddy. The chuckles from the public section of the court grew loud enough to elicit a stern frown from the Magistrate. In response to the Magistrate's somewhat ironic query as to whether he was willing to take the oath, Paddy refused to answer. The Magistrate graciously commented that in this particular instance he would not insist the parrot take the oath nor charge it with contempt of court. Clancy was granted permission to question the parrot and the Magistrate would consider any evidence it might offer in support of his case that Mr Tobias Totten had under-delivered him by one bag of coal.

"Thank you, m'lord your honour sir," said Clancy as he turned and addressed the parrot on the chair beside him. "Paddy. Coalman deliver coal. How many bags?"

Paddy took a keen interest in the Magistrate. Also in the Clerk of the Court. Indeed, of the entire courtroom and everyone and everything in it. He looked around and up and down. Then around and up and down again. But he spoke not a word.

"C'mon Paddy," coaxed Clancy. "Coalman? How many bags?"

Paddy uttered not a word. Clancy rattled his finger across the wires of the cage to get some sort of reaction. "Come on now, Paddy," he pleaded. "Coalman. How many bags did coalman leave?" He pointed to the Magistrate. "Tell the nice man. How many bags?"

Paddy made not a sound of any sort despite Clancy's repeated coaxing. But he continued to display a great but silent interest in everything around him, much to the amusement of the general public and the annoyance of the Magistrate. Clancy shook Paddy's cage violently. "Paddy!" he shouted. "You were there! You told me! Tell me again! How many bags of coal! It was three bags! Wasn't it! Three bags!" It was at this point when unbridled and unchecked laughter erupted all around the court and the defence counsel for Tobias accused Clancy of leading the witness that the Magistrate's patience finally ran out. He demanded immediate order in his court and instructed Clancy to step down from the witness stand and take his bird with him and consider himself very lucky he did not find himself facing a charge of wasting the court's time.

Although nothing in the way of hard evidence, from either Clancy or his parrot, had been presented to prove Tobias had short-delivered Clancy's coal, the Magistrate called the coalman to take the stand.

"Mr Totten," began the Magistrate, "as far as I can make any sense of this nonsense, which has been foolishly brought before me, Mr McCrory paid you an amount of money to deliver, in his absence, to his residence, four bags of coal. Is this correct?"

"Very correct, Your Honour," answered Tobias.

"How many bags did you deliver?"

"Four bags, Your Honour."

The Magistrate paused. He stroked his chin solemnly. "Were you aware, Mr Totten, that at the time you were delivering the coal, Mr McCrory's parrot – Paddy – was in the window watching – and – and, ahem – according to Mr McCrory, counting the number of bags you delivered?"

Tobias nodded. "I knew the parrot was there. I could see it. But I didn't know it was countin' the bags. I didn't know parrots could count. I still don't think parrots can count. Anyway, it makes no difference to me. I was paid to leave four bags. I left four bags."

"One final question, Mr Totten," pressed the Magistrate. "Did you obtain any sort of receipt for the bags of coal you delivered?"

Tobias laughed out loud. "Receipt? You must be jokin'! There was nobody there but the parrot. Don't tell me that oul' bird has a degree in English as well as Mathematics!"

The entire courtroom, including the Clerk of the Court but excluding the Magistrate, exploded in a convulsion of loud raucous laughter. Clancy glared daggers at his former coalman and the Magistrate threatened to clear the court immediately if order was not restored forthwith. Order was restored, though not quite as quickly as the Magistrate requested. But Clancy had failed miserably to produce any evidence that Tobias Totten had short-delivered his bags of coal. The case was thrown out of court and Clancy and his parrot with it.

That was a hard and bitter day for Clancy, even worse than the day he had been left to stand alone at the altar. He became the laughing stock of Newtownards and the entire peninsula. To his credit he bore no ill will to Paddy who on the witness stand had for whatever reason failed to repeat in court the statements he had declared with such assertion to Clancy that Tobias had left only three bags of coal.

But yet another heavy blow was to fall upon the lonely, depressed, and demoralised Clancy. The local papers gave the unusual court case extensive coverage. Paddy the parrot's photograph was splashed all over the front pages. Paddy was immediately identified as having escaped from a nice little mansion on Donaghadee's Warren Road. His legitimate owner was able to quote the numbers on the ring on Paddy's leg and establish the fact the bird belonged to him. Paddy had counted his last bag of coal. Very shortly after his appearance in court and his photograph in the newspapers, Paddy returned to a life of luxury and central heating in his original home overlooking the Copeland Islands where he would never need to count another bag of coal.

Clancy never recovered from the indignity of his day in court. It drove him more and more into himself and as far away as possible from any fellow member of the human race. In his remaining years, and they were lonely years, Clancy was rarely seen, apart from the odd occasion when he ventured into Greyabbey for the bag of turf, which he wheeled back out home on the bar of his bike. To this day, Tobias Totten is the only one who knows how many bags of coal were delivered on that day which drove Clancy over the edge of normality. Only Tobias. And maybe Paddy. Paddy the Parrot, who never spoke another word after the fateful day he took the stand as the witness for the prosecution.

Voices in the Ether

Some dark and windy night, if you have occasion to take that twisted hill road that runs up from the town of Newtownards toward Belfast, make sure you don't go on foot. Aye, and above all, make sure you don't go alone. That road is named after mad Bradshaw. And it's well named. Oh, a dark and fearsome place it is on a wild winter night with the wind howling and screeching through the trees like a demented banshee and the branches shaking and shuddering like ghostly figures of long ago and the very vault of heaven itself shut up in a desolation of darkness.

They say there are ghosts about this place, and all within a stone's throw of the Downtown Radio station. And why shouldn't there be? I used to spend quite a bit of time down in the old Greenwell Street, in the oldest part of Newton, at the quaint wee home of oul' Rab M'Gilton. Rab, and his ancient cronies who gathered there every Saturday night, was a fountain of knowledge about the Ards and all its folklore. When everybody was assembled in, Rab would stretch out his legs before the fire, open the whisky bottle, light his battered pipe, take a deep sigh, and commence to regale us with all the terrible things that happened around Newton. And in particular up Bradshaw's Brae where they were building that new radio station.

Rab told us there had been a priory up there, a hanging tree, a drowning well and a graveyard, or at least the memory of them, all lying in the same bit of ground. Aye, and as we sat in the hushed silence broken only by the gentle hissing of the gaslight, Rab's cronies added their own tales of the mysteries of that place, which, as every good storyteller would claim, were as true, "as sure as they were sittin' on this sate!" Some of them whispered tales of seeing mad Bradshaw, the man the brae is named after, lashing his coach and horses up the hill after a night's wild drinking in Newtownards, the horses foaming at the mouth and the sparks flying from their hooves like the fires of hell on the dark lonely road. Aye. And Bradshaw and his horses dead for many a long year before the old men who told the story were ever born.

Rab said there was a graveyard at the other side of the road from where they were building that Downtown Radio. You didn't know there was a graveyard there? Well, just take a look over the hedge the next time you're up that way. Strange and unholy acts, and shameful things happened there, even when that place was in use for the solemn purpose it was created for so long ago. Most of the folk who lie there had little of this world's gold or goods. Most of them were lowered into the rough bit of ground with not even a marker to tell they had ever walked the face of the earth. But if you look closely you'll see the indentation of the graves in that mournful place.

Kiltonga, for that's what they call the place opposite the graveyard, is so much steeped in history and mystery that nobody knows the half of it. Nobody knows what is true, what might be true, or what is not true. Kiltonga was a place of thick woods through which the sunlight rarely entered, much less the foot of man. But they say there was a monastery there, the church of Tonga, not far from the foot of Scrabo Hill. It may be monks worshipped and prayed and chanted and died here, close to the Downtown studios. Voices going out into the ether then. Voices going out into the ether now.

Then the Quakers came. Their wee house of worship is still standing. If, some night, you chance to wander on that lonely road, you'll pass it by on the way to Downtown Radio. On a moonlight night, if you're brave enough to walk up there, with the graveyard on your right hand and the wee church on the left, you might imagine you see figures flitting behind the narrow windows. But maybe it's only a trick of the moonlight through the trees. Maybe it's only a trick of the moonlight.

Aye, it was a secret place, Kiltonga, and well hidden from the hurrying cares of the outside world. But then, further back, deeper into the woods, they cut down the trees, and the place where holy men lived and toiled and died was levelled and cleared. Downtown Radio was established and voices were heard again in that place. But now the voices were not confined to the place of their utterance. They reached out into the heavens and were carried all across the land. They say one of the Downtown studios is built on the site of an ancient well where a young girl drowned a long, long time ago. Whether it's true or not, the story goes that a lady in white haunts the corridors of Downtown Radio. I've worked in those studios. Oh, it's all very well in the hustle and bustle of the newsroom where everything is light and noise and excitement and people and information come and go so fast nobody has time to think. But close the newsroom door behind you and walk down one of those lonely corridors to a dimly lit studio where you are on your own, isolated, cut off from the outside world in your little soundproof room. Soundproofed so not a sound can come in. Soundproofed, so not a cry of yours can go out....

And what about the spirits of holy men and monks and the native people of this place who dwelt once upon a time on the same piece of ground? What other spirits even yet glide silently unseen within Downtown Radio itself? Perhaps they stand motionless, unseen, in the corner of the Downtown studio late at night, observing the lone presenter, listening to these strange new chants and music, which issue forth from invisible souls without bodies. What do they make of it? Chanting in the ether then. Chanting in the ether now.

And you, dear reader. Disciple of the high tech and vision age where all the world and what it holds is at your command with the touch of a button. Perhaps you laugh all this to scorn. Well, maybe you should walk up that hilly and twisted road that runs up from Newtownards and past Kiltonga. Not on a balmy summer day when the warm bright sun beams down from above Scrabo and the sky is blue and blackbirds and thrushes warble happily in the thicket and all is well with the world. Oh no. Not then. Take the road, if you will, late on a dark and wild winter night when the sky is black as pitch and the thunder rolls and the lightning flashes and the wind howls and screeches and the natural world, of which you are a merely a tiny insignificant part, is in control. Listen, if you will, above the howling and the shuddering of nature. Listen for the sounds of times gone. And watch. Watch among the darkness and the lightning for the visions of things that used to be, perhaps are no more and yet maybe still are. But be sure you go on foot. Oh yes, be sure to go on foot. And if you're brave enough, go alone. Yes. Go alone. Maybe then you will be humbled. Maybe then you will learn the mystery of the drowning well, the hanging tree, the old graveyard where terrible things happened and of the hooded chanters. And maybe, if you listen, carefully, very carefully, you will hear again, from the days of long, long ago, those other voices. The voices in the ether.

Scrape the Beetle

It was from oul' Rab M'Gilton, on yet another winter night of storytelling around the turf fire by the light of the hissing gaslight, over forty years ago, that I first heard the awful story of "scrape the beetle". Rab spoke of the participants in the terrible tale which shook Newtownards town as if he had known each of them personally. He certainly would have been alive at the time the events took place, probably just coming out of childhood. It is very likely he knew by sight and may even have been on speaking terms with at least some of the characters involved in the tale which has passed into Newtownards folklore and is still recalled to this very day. But whereas doubt could have been thrown on many of the yarns Rab spun about the old Ards, Saturday night after Saturday night, when he'd fortified himself from his whisky bottle, this one was different. Very different. This story needed no embellishment. This story was true.

Willie Quinn was one of the most popular and respected young men in Newtownards, without an enemy in the world. He had come to live in the town when his stepfather, Samuel Heron, manager of the local Ulster Print Works, married Willie's widowed mother Agnes Quinn. On the death of Willie's mother, Samuel Heron became the young man's legal guardian. Samuel Heron married again, for the third time, but Willie continued to dwell in Flush Hall, his stepfather's home, with the rest of Heron's family.

Flush Hall was an impressive, lonely house standing in its own grounds beneath the shadow of Scrabo Hill at the top left hand side of the Scrabo Road. An avenue about fifty yards long, secured by two large white pillars and a pair of iron gates, ran up to the dwelling house. The house was owned by the Ulster Print Works and rented by Samuel Heron from his employers. The secluded house was home not only to Willie Quinn, but also Samuel Heron's own children, including Samuel junior, and Heron's third wife Bessie. But Willie Quinn would soon quit the secluded old house forever. He had already paid a visit to Ballynahinch to obtain a marriage licence. On the 18th of February 1915, in a matter of days, he would marry his sweetheart, Newtownards girl, Miss Minnie Lavery. The honeymoon would be spent with relatives in Newry, Willie's hometown. Then Willie and his new bride would return to Newtownards to set up their own home at number 34 John Street Lane.

Willie Quinn, twenty-three years of age, was indeed a very popular personality in Newtownards and much farther afield. He was a keen supporter of Ards Football Club and could usually be found at all their games, whether they were played at home or away. He was a member of the Orange Institution and the Masons. The young man had a very fine singing voice and was a member of both the Newtownards Male Choir and the Ards Minstrel Troupe and Willie's vocal talents led to his being in great demand to perform at social and charitable evenings, both in Newtownards and across the County. Willie gave of his talents and time without charge. He loved music and song and was always pleased to be in "the concord of sweet words".

Willie was employed as a clerk in the Ulster Print Works, a large sombre looking building only a few yards from Flush Hall. His salary was £1 a week. But Willie would not be without means when he quit Flush Hall and started out on married life. Upon the death of his mother Willie had inherited seven houses in Newry, five in Mary Street and two in Chapel Street. Willie's stepfather, Samuel Heron, had been made trustee of Willie's estate until he should come of age. Accumulated rents to the approximate value of about £300 from Willie's property had already been made payable to his stepfather. Although almost three years had passed since Willie had come of age and he had made representation to his stepfather for some of the money to be made available to help him set up house, none had been forthcoming. Now, with marriage imminent and new responsibilities upon his shoulders, Willie had good reason to believe the transference of the funds would soon be made, as his stepfather had said they would. Life was looking extremely good for the popular Willie Quinn.

According to Willie's chum, Henry (Harry) Aicken, on the night of February 13th, 1915, a cold, dark and windy night, the pair had been to a meeting at the Masonic Hall in James Street. At about 9.40pm they went to Wallace's public house, popularly known in more recent times as "Yankee Wallace's", in Regent Street. Willie had a bottle of stout and a bottle of ale. The friends left the pub at about 11.30pm. When they finally said goodnight and parted, Henry turned toward the direction of the Square to buy some cigarettes in Mr Jamison's before returning to his home at number 2 Ann Street. Willie headed toward Frederick Street and Mill Street and the Scrabo Road. He was a quick walker. It would take him fifteen or twenty minutes to reach the white stone pillars and the iron entrance gates of Flush Hall. He would be there by midnight.

It was about midnight when Mrs Bessie Heron, who was in bed, heard a noise like the quarrelling of dogs at the front of the house. It lasted about a minute or two. Fifteen or twenty minutes later she got up and went into her husband's room to ask if he had heard anything. Her husband was not there. She returned to her husband's room again some time later. It was still empty. Heron's son, Samuel Heron junior, slept in the same bedroom as his father. Bessie wakened him and asked him if he knew where his father was. The eighteen-year-old boy said he did not know where his father was. He pulled on some clothes and he and Bessie went to see if Willie was in his room. He was not.

Bessie lit the gaslight on the landing. Accompanied by Samuel junior, she went downstairs. The pair had only reached the bottom of the stairs when they saw Samuel Heron come in to the house by the front door. Bessie estimated the time to be about twelve-thirty. In response to his family's queries as to whether he had heard a noise, Heron said he had gone to look about the door but could see or hear nothing. The family returned to their beds.

After returning to bed Bessie fell asleep. She was awakened again by the ringing of the front door bell. She lay on in bed, waiting and listening. After some time the bell rang again. Bessie got up. She got a light and went to the front door and asked who was there. She heard her stepson Willie answer. "It's me, Bessie," he said. "I want a hand."

Bessie unlocked and opened the door. Willie was sitting in the corner of the porch. He was thoroughly dishevelled and covered in dirt and blood. Willie said, "Come on in 'til I get warmed. I am very cold". She brought him into the kitchen and sat him down on the sofa. At that point Samuel Heron came downstairs shouting, "What is that? What's wrong?" Bessie cried, "Come down quick. Willie is badly hurt."

As Bessie prepared to return upstairs to tend to one of the children who was crying, Heron asked Willie what had happened. Willie told him he had only just got inside the gate when some "blighter" struck him with something heavy, which almost knocked him down.

Willie's face was covered with blood and dirt and soil. Heron washed Willie's head and face, needing two buckets of water to clean away the mixture of blood and dirt on the wounds. Heron prepared a hot milky drink, to which he added some spirits, and gave it to his stepson. Willie told him he wanted to go to bed. Heron helped him upstairs and undressed him and got him into bed. Willie appeared to be comfortable but again complained of being cold. No doubt the young man was suffering from shock as a result of his beating. Heron found another quilt and put it on his stepson's bed and then returned to his own bedroom. He checked on Willie several times before retiring to bed. It was now about half past six on Sunday morning. Heron did not summon the police in an effort to apprehend the person or persons who had launched such a vicious attack on his stepson. Neither did he call a doctor to tend to Willie's injuries.

Heron arose somewhere between eight and nine o'clock. He took a hot drink in to Willie, and asked him how he was. Willie replied, "I'm all right." Heron had his breakfast and then cycled about a mile across the town to get the doctor. Before setting out on the journey he examined the driveway leading from the door of the house to the front gates. He found bloodstains on the gravel and a clot of blood. He also found Willie's row of false teeth and a glove. When he returned from the bicycle ride to the doctor's he examined Willie's clothes. He told Willie his watch, which had belonged to Willie's grandfather, was missing. So was his pocketbook. There was no money at all in his trousers. When he informed Willie of this loss his stepson said, "My God, I've been robbed." Willie told Heron he had two £1 notes, a ten-shilling note, and a few loose shillings on his person when he was attacked.

Dr. Jamison was unwell and in bed when he received Heron's message asking him to come to examine his stepson as he had got a bad beating and he was afraid of anything happening to him. The doctor arrived at Flush Hall between ten and ten-thirty. He found Willie in bed with his head bandaged with clean cloths.

He removed the cloths and examined Willie wounds, which were very dirty and covered with blood, soil and manure from the garden. There was a wound on the left temple about two inches in length and a small wound half an inch long beneath it. The doctor found another wound above the left ear and two ragged wounds on the back of the head. The left side of Willie's face was swollen and the left eye almost closed. The doctor cleaned and stitched the wounds and re-dressed them.

Dr. Jamison asked Willie to walk a few paces about the room, which he did without any problem. At this point Willie was perfectly rational and the doctor could find nothing else wrong with him. He got the impression Willie did not know who had struck him when he came through the gates late on the Saturday night. When the doctor was about to depart Heron asked him if he should report the matter to the police. Dr. Jamison told him he didn't look at all well himself and to wait a bit until he had calmed down. At that point the doctor did not believe Willie Quinn's injuries were life threatening.

At about six o'clock that evening Willie's fiancée, Miss Minnie Lavery, who lived on the Portaferry Road, received a note from Heron. It read: 'You might take a walk up as soon as you can, as Willie wants to see you. Yours sincerely, S. Heron.' The note made no mention of the fact Willie had been hurt.

Miss Lavery cancelled her intention of going to church as she usually did and went instead to Flush Hall. Heron took her to Willie's bedroom and on the way up told her Willie had been hurt. Willie was asleep when Miss Lavery entered the room. Heron wakened him but did not afford the couple much in the way of privacy. He moved in and out of the bedroom during the entire time of Miss Lavery's visit and when he did leave the room he did not close the door behind him.

Willie dozed and wakened every few minutes. But Miss Lavery did manage to speak to her fiancé and ask him what had happened. Willie replied, "I think the Germans have got me."

As a result of information passed to them Head Constable

Maclaine and Sergeant Reynolds visited Flush Hall at about 8.00pm in the evening. Herron admitted them to the house. "How is Willie Quinn?" asked Maclaine of Heron. "I hear he has been assaulted and robbed."

"Quinn is now asleep," replied Heron and invited Maclaine and Reynolds into the drawing room. He then gave a statement to Maclaine of what he had seen and heard on the night Willie was attacked and informed Maclaine he had not reported the matter to the police because it was Sunday and he had not wanted to bother them. He went on to say he believed the attack was not meant for Willie, but for himself and he was always in dread when he passed the Model School late at night. He intended to purchase a revolver and carry it in his hand on future journeys home from the town. Maclaine and Reynolds left without seeing Willie.

Later that night Maclaine, this time with Sergeant M. Duffy, returned. When Heron answered the ring of the doorbell he informed Maclaine that Willie was still asleep. Maclaine said he wished to see him anyhow and he and Duffy passed up the stairs accompanied by Heron. When Maclaine and Duffy entered Willie's room they found him not asleep, but wide-awake and quite sensible.

Maclaine questioned Willie about the traumatic events that had happened to him. Willie told him: 'I remained in the billiard-room, Town Hall, until closing time, at about eleven o'clock on Saturday night. (This is at variance to the evidence given by Harry Aicken that the pair had spent some time in Wallace's pub. This may have been genuine confusion on the part of a man still suffering shock from the effects of a bad beating or it may be he did not wish it to be known he had been in a public house – assuming Aicken's evidence was correct.) I left in the company of Harry Aicken and a few others. Harry Aicken accompanied me up Regent Street to Kerlin's corner at the end of Gibson's Lane. We remained there chatting for some time. We parted at about a quarter to twelve and I went home through Frederick Street and Mill Street. When I had passed through the gate at Flush Hall I banged the right half of the gate behind me to close it and was walking toward the house when I heard footsteps behind me. I turned round and saw a man bigger than myself make to strike me with something like a mallet. The man never spoke. He came from behind the right pillar going out, or left coming in. I ducked the first blow, but the second struck me above the left eye and knocked me down. The next I remember was seeing the man between the house and me. I shouted and ran toward the house. I was struck two or three times after and became unconscious. It was about midnight at the time. I thought I was only a short time unconscious and when I came to I crawled to the door and rang the bell and the missus let me in.'

Actually Willie had lain unconscious on the cold February night for much longer than he had imagined. It was probably four or five hours after the brutal attack that he came to and crawled to the door of Flush Hall and cried out for assistance. Dr. Warnock, at the request of Dr. Jamison who was still unwell, attended Willie Quinn at Flush Hall on Monday morning at 11.50am. He gave Willie an injection of anti-tetanic [tetanus] serum as suggested by Dr. Jamison who thought the wounds might be infected by the amount of horse manure and soil he had found on Willie's head when he had first dressed the injuries. Dr. Warnock again cleaned the wounds and re-dressed them and went home. He had only been at home a few moments when he was called back to Flush Hall.

When the doctor returned to Willie's bedside for the second time the young man appeared to be just coming out of some sort of fit. His breathing was now stertorous, his pulse very rapid and failing quickly. At twenty minutes to three Willie Quinn succumbed to the terrible injuries he had received at the hands of a person or persons unknown in the driveway of Flush Hall on the previous Saturday night or early hours of Sunday morning.

Dr. Jamison, with Dr. Warnock, carried out the autopsy on Willie's body. All the deceased's organs were healthy. Death had come about because of compression of the brain due to haemorrhage through fracture of the skull as a result of violence. Dr. Warnock indicated it was unlikely the wounds would have been sustained through a fall, but rather by a man's fists. However the doctor considered the injuries were inflicted by an attack made on the deceased with the use of a blunt instrument or kicks while he lay on the ground. At the inquest a verdict was brought in that Willie Quinn had been murdered by person or persons unknown.

The cold-blooded murder of such a popular young man caused a sensation among the citizens in the shocked town of Newtownards. Rumours flew about with abandon as to who was responsible for the dastardly deed. So incensed were the townspeople comments were made to the effect that if Willie's murderer could be found and made available to them justice would be carried out without the necessity of any court case or trial. Even the reporter for the *Chronicle* momentarily laid aside his mantle of professionalism while covering the case and wrote 'A personal recollection is that on Christmas night he, (Willie) with a number of the best known vocal artistes in the town, honoured us with the favour of their company. What an enjoyable few hours we spent listening to Christmas carols, humorous and sentimental songs, solos, duets, quartettes, and choruses, in all of which our esteemed young friend took a leading part.'

If these were the feelings of friends and acquaintances, what can have been the heart-rending pain and sorrow and shock carried in the heart of Miss Minnie Lavery, the young lady who had planned to become Willie's wife in just a few days time. In an instant, her life had changed forever.

Willie Quinn's funeral was arranged to take place in his hometown of Newry on Thursday the 18th February. The service would be conducted in St Patrick's Church, the church where Willie had been baptised. The Rev. William Moore, who had been Willie's Sunday school teacher, would take the service. Before eleven o'clock on the morning of the funeral large crowds gathered on the Scrabo Road, and particularly in the vicinity of Flush Hall, to pay their last tribute to the young man they had all known and respected. Behind the gates the avenue up to Flush Hall was lined with dozens of members of the Orange and Masonic Institutions. They would walk in orderly fashion behind Willie's oak coffin. The inscription on the brass plate of the coffin read simply:

William Quinn
Died 15th February 1915

The many floral tributes included those from the Town Hall Billiard Club and the officers and members of L.O.L. 872. There was also a wreath from Willie's friends in the Ards Minstrel Troupe, in whose company he had spent many a happy hour. Sadly, Willie would sing and entertain and join in "the sweet concorde of words" no more. The cortege was due to depart Flush Hall at eleven o'clock. Unfortunately there was some confusion regarding the motor transport required to carry the coffin and chief mourners to Newry. Hasty telephones calls had to be made to Belfast before a motor hearse was secured from Mr Adam Turner. It was about half an hour after mid-day when the cortege finally left Flush Hall. The huge crowds waiting outside the iron gates were very much moved as it turned out of the avenue and passed them by. Many women shed tears as the cortege wound its way down the Scrabo Road and part of Mill Street before turning into Frederick Street and then Church Street toward the Belfast Road. The sad procession eventually reached the railway bridge at the end of Church Street and the commencement of the Belfast Road. It was at this point a very dramatic incident happened.

The cortege stopped just beyond the bridge to allow relatives and mourners to enter the motor vehicles for the long journey to Newry. Immediately Head Constable Maclaine stepped forward.

He touched Samuel Heron on the shoulder. He cautioned him and charged him with the murder of William Quinn.

"I won't hesitate," replied Heron. "I am going back with you. I expected this."

Heron shook hands with his son and some friends who bade him goodbye. Heron replied, "It's not goodbye, it will be all right yet." A vehicle was taken out from the cortege. Heron was placed in it and immediately driven to the Newtownards police barracks where he was detained. This dramatic turn of events caused another sensation in the town. All sorts of rumours and stories spread like wildfire across the Ards while the cortege travelled on to Newry.

At four o'clock in the afternoon the cortege reached Newry town. It was met by large crowds of people of all classes and creed testifying to the honour in which Willie had been held in his hometown, and as a mark of sympathy for his surviving relatives. St. Patrick's Church was filled to overflowing for the service. The Rev. William Moore, when speaking of the painful circumstances that brought them together on this sad day, informed the congregation that Willie had been baptised in St. Patrick's. Willie had attended Sunday school here and he (Rev. Moore) had been his Sunday school teacher.

The Rev. Moore and Rev. D.H. Maconachie of Strean Presbyterian Church in Newtownards conducted the service at the graveside. On the day he was to be joined with Miss Minnie Lavery in holy matrimony, Willie Quinn's body was laid in its last resting place.

A special Court of petty sessions was held in the police barracks in Newtownards at six o'clock in the evening of the day Willie Quinn was buried. Herron was remanded until Friday morning and ordered to be removed to Belfast jail where he would be held overnight. Large crowds of shocked and bemused citizens gathered at the town's railway station in Victoria Avenue and on the streets leading to it to see Heron conveyed to Belfast jail on the 7.50pm train. In their lifetime, quiet, peaceful Newtownards had never witnessed anything like the last few awful days.

Heron was brought back to Newtownards at eleven o'clock next morning to attend the Magisterial Inquiry in Newtownards Courthouse. The crowds who gathered outside were extremely annoyed to learn they would not be permitted to enter. Only those legally involved in the matter and the representatives of the press were allowed in to the courthouse to hear Samuel Heron charged that he did wilfully, feloniously and with malice aforethought murder William Quinn, at Corporation South, Newtownards, on the night of the 13th or morning of the 14th February. In the month of July Samuel Heron was returned for trial at Downpatrick for the murder of his stepson.

Locally, the Flush Hall murder has always, since the time of the awful deed, been popularly known and referred to by the term "scrape the beetle." This unusual term of reference came about as a result of the evidence given by one of the witnesses at the trial. Even today, ninety years after the events, the mention of "scrape the beetle" will bring forth a discourse from anyone of true Ards descent of his version of what happened on the night Willie Quinn was murdered.

On the first day of his trial at Downpatrick, when asked how he pleaded to the charge of murdering William Quinn, Samuel Heron replied in a clear and steady voice, "Not Guilty."

John McBride, a finisher in The Ulster Print Works, of which the accused was Manager, gave evidence and stated he was in the company of Heron on Tuesday 16th February. Heron told him he (Heron) might be arrested on suspicion of Willie's murder. Continuing his evidence McBride stated: "I got a message from Mr Heron on Wednesday evening 17th, [afternoon?] that he wanted to see me, in consequence of which I went to Flush Hall about 2.30 or 2.45 o'clock. He said 'If anything happens to me you may sell the pigeons. You can also sell the poultry and take one of my dogs to your house. Also take my bicycle to Mr Carse's and he can send what is the value of it to my missus.' I came away then and he said 'Wait a minute. I still want you.' He asked me to look below the tank at the mill chimney and I would get the old watch there, as he had got it, and like an old fool went and hid it there.

He then took me into the scullery and said 'I wonder is there anything here that they might look for, as I don't want them to get anything, say for instance, this' - pointing to a beetle [a wooden mallet type instrument used for hammering meat or pounding clothes in a wash-tub] which he lifted and held below the hot water tap in the jaw-box (sink) in the scullery. He said 'You might give that a rub while I see if there is anyone about'. I gave it a rub with a brush and Mr Heron went out of the scullery but he came back immediately and said 'Do you see any marks on it?' I said 'No, not that I can see.' He held it below the hot water tap. I then thought I saw some sort of stain on it while the water was on it. Mr Heron dried it over the gas stove. He did not seem satisfied and got a piece of black emery paper and started rubbing the beetle. He said if he had a bit of sandpaper it might help. He asked me to go to the works to a man named Muir and I would get a piece. I got the piece from Muir, in the presence of Walter Waugh. I took it down to Mr Heron and he took it into the scullery and gave the beetle a rub with it. He said to me 'Take you it into the pantry and give it a rub while I see to the door.' When he went to the door I gave it a slight rub with the sandpaper. Heron was at the door leading to the kitchen. I put it under the hot water tap and Heron turned the water on.

While we were there Mrs Heron went through into the pantry and back again into the kitchen. No one said anything. Mr Heron took the beetle from me and dried it on the gas stove. He asked me if I had a sharp knife, but I did not say anything. He took his own knife and started to scrape the beetle. I said to him

"If you have any suspicions of the thing, why don't you burn it?" He said 'No, they may have seen this thing and might ask for it.'

Head Constable Maclaine gave evidence that on the 20th February he accompanied Sergeant Duffy to the Ulster Print Works and observed the Sergeant remove a watch from underneath a water tank near the chimney. On the same date Maclaine himself found the back of the watch underneath the floor of Heron's office in the factory. On the 21st of February Maclaine and Duffy visited Flush Hall and took possession of a beetle and two pieces of emery paper. Among other items removed from the house was a blood-saturated glove found under the jaw-box in the scullery.

Dr. Robert M. Bronte, specialist in pathology, Dublin, testified as to the result of his examination of several articles, including a beetle, brought to him by Sergeant Duffy. The outer surface of the beetle head was quite smooth with a few small darkish marks. On the face of the beetle were two small cracks. He extended one of the cracks and found human blood at the broken surfaces. Dr. Bronte was absolutely satisfied these bloodstains were of human origin.

Robert Stoupe, a watchmaker in Newtownards, identified the watch found at the Ulster Print Works. It was a gent's English single lever watch; silver dialled, and bore the number 4896. The maker's name, Marshall of Newry, was inscribed on the works and the case bore the "Tiger" hallmark. He had repaired the watch several times. The timepiece was recorded in Mr Stoupe's records as belonging to William Quinn.

The jury heard evidence that as Willie Quinn's legal guardian, rents of approximately £300 from Willie's properties in Newry had been paid directly to his stepfather. Although Willie had asked his stepfather for some of this money to help him set up his new home in John Street Lane, and Heron had promised him it would be forthcoming and there would be a settlement, Willie had received nothing.

The accused was also pressed for money on other accounts.

In 1911 he had borrowed £1000 from James K. A. Robb of Charleyville. That amount, plus interest, was still due. Robb's solicitor stated Heron had agreed to pay £75 of the amount in February. He failed to keep his promise. The Newtownards Branch of the Belfast Bank was owed £215-1-4 in respect of an overdraft. The bank had a guarantee for the amount. The accused owed the Newtownards Branch of the Ulster Bank £26-3-6 for which there was no security. Heron was £75 in debt to the Lisburn Loan Discount Company. Thomas Drake, provision merchant, Newtownards, was owed £61-13-1, Hugh Donnan, seed and hardware merchant, Newtownards, was owed £21-2-2. Simms and Co, drapers, was owed £17-0-5, Mrs Caughey, undertaker, for whom W. L. Doggart worked, was owed £11-11-4. Heron, as trustee of the Newry property, owed Mrs Massey, Willie Quinn's aunt, approximately £25 in respect of an annuity of five shillings a week.

The prosecution also pointed out that despite the horrific attack made upon his stepson Heron had made no attempt to find a doctor and have his injuries attended to until much later in the morning and after he had partaken of his breakfast. Neither did he report the attack to the police in an attempt to have the attacker or attackers apprehended. Heron was the only person with the reasons for and the means of murdering Willie Quinn.

Mr Brown, for the defence, stated the entire case against Samuel Heron was of a circumstantial nature only. Willie Quinn had been unable to identify his attacker. From the rents of the Newry properties belonging to Willie Quinn and paid to Heron, Heron had housed, fed, clothed and educated his stepson and provided him with pocket money. When these expenses had been met there was little or nothing remaining. Upon Willie's death, all monies and property belonging to him reverted to his aunts, so Heron was not at any advantage by killing his stepson. There could well be bloodstains on a beetle used for everyday purposes in a normal household. Mr Brown cast doubt upon John McBride's evidence as he had claimed he had seen the accused scrape the beetle and claiming only he and the accused had been in the scullery at that time. In his evidence Sergeant Duffy had stated he was in the scullery at the time stated by McBride and had not seen him. The defence was confident the jury would give the accused the consideration his case deserved and they would not find him guilty unless the evidence forced them to do so.

At the end of his lengthy summing up the judge reminded the jury the accused was entitled to the benefit of any doubt that may be in their mind. The decision, innocent or guilty, was theirs and theirs alone. The jury retired to arrive at their verdict at 12.35pm. They returned at 2.56pm. They could not agree on a verdict. The jury was discharged and Samuel Heron was returned to the cells and remanded until the next Assizes.

Samuel Herron would be tried twice more for the murder of his stepson. Each time, the jury could not reach a verdict. At the conclusion of the third trial Heron was acquitted and stepped down, a free man. But his life and position in Newtownards was ruined. He was ostracised by his fellow citizens. Many people were afraid of him and he was rarely seen about the town, at least not in daylight. He eventually took ship to Australia. For a while there were reported sightings of him by a few folk who for one reason or another chanced upon those faraway shores. Then he faded from the scene of time. But whether the term is deserved or not, to this very day Samuel Heron is remembered in the town of Newtownards as "scrape the beetle".

Flush Hall was demolished many years later. The edge of the Scrabo housing estate covers the ground where it once stood and where Willie's awful murder took place. The Ulster Print Works has disappeared in the last few years. A graceful old people's home now stands in place of the building which held so many clues to that terrible crime. However, the front facade still stands, the last physical reminder of the events of all those years ago. Perhaps most ironic of all, the beetle which allegedly was used to batter Willie Quinn to his death, had been specially made for him as a prop to use when he acted the part of a policeman in one of the many theatrical pieces he performed on local stages.

Willie's fiancée, Miss Minnie Lavery, never married. In later years she kept a small shop on the Conway Square side of the town's High Street, close to where the pedestrian crossing is now situated. The author remembers the neat, quiet, dignified little lady being pointed out to him, many years ago, as she walked to her home on the Portaferry Road.

Many lives were changed and ruined forever on the night of the 13th February 1915. Willie Quinn lost most. But perhaps the heaviest burden, carried for a lifetime of years with quiet dignity and silence, was laid upon Miss Lavery. Time takes all its children. Miss Lavery has also gone, united at last, we trust, with Willie Quinn, her one true love. The name of Samuel Herron may also fade and pass away. But it appears the man himself is destined to be remembered forever by the awful name given to him by the people of the Ards after the terrible event of almost one hundred years ago. Scrape the beetle.

A Wee Bit of Christmas Crack

Oul' Rab M'Gilton was indeed a great man at spinning the yarns. Whether they were always true, or not, it was difficult to say. But oul' Rab had a way of weaving a tale that left you in no doubt every last detail of it had actually happened exactly the way Rab described it. And round about Christmas time, year after year, nothing gave Rab more delight than to relate once again the plight that befell an oul' crony of his on a certain Christmas Eve many years earlier. Rab told the yarn so many times I can still recall every bit of it, though it's well over forty years since I last heard it.

Robert John Henry, a sixty-two year old full-time postman and part-time farmer, pedalled his big and heavy Post Office official issue bicycle up the lonen toward Mick McDaniel's farm. Robert John was beginning to feel his age. Every day that passed made the big red bicycle harder to push. It was even tougher at Christmas time with a load of Christmas cards and parcels to deliver as well as ordinary mail. Worse still on this Christmas Eve with the snow lying in deep drifts and almost over the top of the hedges. Robert John was having trouble staying on the bicycle let alone making any real headway round the countryside. He'd be glad when he reached Mick's place. He could stop for a minute or two for a wee bit of crack before he attempted to ascend Lizzie Reid's terrible hill to deliver the Christmas card from her brother in Australia.

Robert John reached the end of the lonen and steered the big bicycle erratically into Mick's farmyard, scattering two or three bemused hens and a couple of ducks scraping about in the snow in a vain attempt to find something to eat. He dismounted and let the bicycle fall against the gable wall of Mick's tumbledown farmhouse. Robert John rummaged about in the big canvas bag in the carrier of the bicycle and hoked out a couple of letters. He stuck them in his pocket, stamped the snow from his boots and hammered his fist on the door.

Those were the days when doors were never locked, but always left on the latch. A neighbour or friend calling at any house in the countryside simply knocked on the door and walked in, usually without waiting for an invitation to do so. But Robert John Henry was not visiting as a private individual. He was on official Post Office business so he waited for the invitation to enter. It came immediately.

"Come on, on in," bawled Mick from inside the house. "The door's open. Come on in!"

Robert John lifted the latch and pushed open the door. He was immediately met by a room full of billowing and dense sweet-smelling turf smoke which so filled Mick's abode the postman could barely make out the form of the old farmer lying sprawled in his battered chair before the hearth.

"Ah, it's yourself, Robert John," coughed Mick as he looked up from somewhere in the smoke. "Come on in and give us a wee bit of your Christmas crack. Pull up a chair and set yourself down."

Robert John shuffled his way through the gloom and the smoke toward the sound of Mick's voice and the faint glow of the reeking turf fire. He pulled up a rickety chair as invited. With a heavy sigh he lowered himself down into the seat.

"Thank ye, Mick. I will indeed sit down a minute to draw my breath. Man dear, that's one hardy mornin'. Just as bad as I have seen."

Mick nodded. "I haven't put my foot over the door yet. I've been tryin' all mornin' to get this oul' fire to light. But I can't get her goin'. No life in her at all. Nothin' but smoke and a promise."

"Och, it'll be the damp in the chimney, Mick," declared Robert John. "And there's no draught either. Ye need a good draught to get a turf fire goin'. But there's not even a breeze – an' the snow lyin' two fut deep. I can hardly get the oul' bike pushed through it. I'm sorry to say it Mick, but I think we're in for a white Christmas."

Mick reached down to the foot of his chair and lifted an almost full bottle of whisky. "Funny you should say that, Robert John. I was listenin' to the wireless last night. I got the battery charged yesterday. The oul' valves lit up like a Tilley lamp – she was goin' like a good 'un. Anyway, your man Crosby was on – the Yankee crooner. He was singin' this new song. And that's what it was called. *White Christmas.*"

"Huh!" snorted Robert John. "That's a daft name fer a song. Who wud want to sing a song about a white Christmas! That'll niver catch on! It's all right lukkin' at snow an' ice an' the robin chirpin' in the holly bush when it's on a Christmas card. It's altogether a different thing when ye're up to yer oxters in the snow an' slush an' tryin' to push a Post Office bike up Lizzie Reid's hill, an' you more often off it than on it. White Christmas! Huh! Crosby's not a bad oul' chanter, an' he might make his name at it. But he'll get nowhere with a song like that. It'll never catch on!"

Mick pulled the cork from his bottle. "You'll take a wee dram, Robert John?" he murmured. "To drive out the cold".

Robert John shook his head. "Thank ye, no, Mick.

Unfortunately I cannot partake. I am here only in my official capacity of deliverin' His Majesty's mail to your good self. I have two letters for ye, one of which I suspect might be a Christmas card." He paused and wiped his brow. "However, if by any stroke of good fortune ye wud happen to have a mug of buttermilk about the place, I would be happy to join ye." He pulled Mick's letters from his pocket and handed them to the old farmer.

Mick took the envelopes from Robert John's outstretched hand and tossed them at the side of the hearth without bothering to look at them. "You're in luck, Robert John. I've a crock full of fresh buttermilk in the scullery," he said, rising to his feet. "Just out of the churn yesterday – aye and the butter floatin' on it like lumps of hen's teeth!" Mick retired to the scullery and shuffled back with a big blue mug overflowing with the aforementioned delicacy. He thrust it into Robert John's hands. "Knock that intil ye, Robert John. That'll slake your thirst!"

Robert John did as he was bid. He took a good quaff of the buttermilk and licked his lips as Mick poured himself half a tumbler of his own favourite liquid, which was not buttermilk. "Boys that's powerful stuff, Mick," grinned the postman as he wiped his lips with the cuff of his jacket. "Powerful! I've said it before, an' I'll say it again. Ye cannot bate a good mug of buttermilk. Man, it goes down the throat like honey. Ye cuddn't bate it!"

Mick nodded and gave a little cough as his first whisky of the day caught at his throat. He leaned toward the smoky glow of the fire and gave the turf a bit of a thump with the poker. He was rewarded with a shower of burning sparks which flew up the chimney and disappeared, leaving the smoking turf as dark as before. "I'm glad you're enjoyin' it, Robert John. It'll get you into the Christmas spirit. Sure another day and Christmas'll be as far away as ever. I know you're not one for the festive season – but maybe you'll be puttin' up a Christmas tree this year?"

Robert John drained the last of his buttermilk. He set the mug at his feet. "Huh! I'll be doin' no such thing, Mick. This whole Christmas business is gettin' out of hand. Did ye know that Bertie

Keenan in the 'Dee had the Christmas decorations in his shop window two full weeks before the twenty-fifth of December! Two full weeks! An' I delivered a card to a wumman on the Killaughey Road who had a Christmas tree stuck in her parlour a full week before Christmas Day! I tell ye, Mick. The whole thing's gettin' out of hand!"

Mick finished off his Cream of the Barley and replenished his glass. He waved the bottle at his visitor. "You'll take just a drop, Robert John? To help you make it up Lizzie's hill?"

Robert John contemplated the whisky bottle. He hesitated. He leaned down and lifted his mug from the floor. "Well, nothin' more than a drop, Mick. Only enough to wet my lips. Just to be sociable – an' seein' it's Christmas. As ye can see, I am engaged on official Post Office business. Partakin' of intoxicatin' liquor while on His Majesty's service is strictly forbidden. It is a sackable offence. I cud loss my pension."

"Hold out your mug," encouraged Mick. "A drop of the cratur'll not do you a button of harm. Sure the buttermilk'll have put a linin' on your stomach. And who's to know about it but you and me? Hold out your mug."

Robert John yielded to temptation and held out his mug. Mick half filled it without too much in the way of protest from the postman. "Good health to ye, Mick," grunted Robert John as he took a fair mouthful of the Cream of the Barley.

"Merry Christmas, Robert John! Down the hatch she goes!" chortled Mick, doing his own glass more than ample justice.

The turf fire began to cheer up and glow warmly, as did Robert John Henry when the Cream of the Barley hit his stomach, seemingly without encountering the buttermilk on its way down. "A Happy Christmas 'til ye, Mick. An' many of them!" grinned the postman. To confirm his sentiments he took another drink from his mug.

"You know, Robert John," said Mick, lifting his bottle from the floor once again, "I often wondered about you. Livin' away out there in the moss, all on your own. Why was it you never took a wife?"

Robert John drained the last of his beverage and wiped his mouth with the back of his hand. "Ah well now, Mick," explained the postman. "Like yerself, I take nothin' to do wi' the weemin' – above biddin' them the time of day. Sure they're as hard as the divil to get on with." He held out his mug. Mick reached over and filled it without any censure from the postman. Robert John thanked Mick and took a not ungenerous sip. "But I coorted one m'self, y'know. Years ago. I hadn't much sense at the time. I was only a slip of a lad. Mind ye, if I say so m'self, she wasn't the worst lukkin' wumman about the countryside. I'll give her that. But when she engaged her tongue in conversation, I can tell ye Mick, it fairly shortened the winter!"

Robert John undid his collar button and loosened his Post Office regulation tie. He pushed his chair back a little from the now blazing fire and enjoyed another mouthful of whisky. "Oh, her and me walked out together for a wee while – about nine or ten years I think it was. We were beginnin' to get on rightly together. But then didn't she up and take this terrible notion of wantin' to get married. An' us only startin' to get to know each other! Had me savin' up all my money as well – not that I was earnin' much in them days. I was on the parcel bike. And then nothin' wud do her but I wud have to give up the fegs as well. Ye see Mick, I was partial to a wee Woodbine. An' here was me thinkin' I was a great fella, goin' along wi' all this. Dang me, I mustn't have been right in the head. A lamb gettin' led to the slaughter. That's what I was, Mick. A lamb gettin' led to the slaughter!"

Robert John ceased momentarily in his discourse to finish his Cream of the Barley. He waved the empty mug at his host. "An' then if it didn't get to the bit where I wasn't allowed to spend a penny of my own hard earned money without enquirin' from the love of my life if I wud be entitled to do so. An' us not even married!"

Robert John, now warming to his work, held out his mug as Mick lifted his bottle and waved it again in his direction. He lodged no complaint as Mick poured a generous measure. Robert John promptly disposed of half the whisky before he continued. "Anyway, it comes to Christmas Eve. Suddenly she's struck down with an awful case of melincooley – I think that's what she called it – I niver heard tell of it – and it appears she's just goin' to fade away an' die right there and then if she's not engaged to be wed on that very day. Hauls me up to Newton on the half-ten bus an' drags me the whole way down High Street to Wallace's the jewellers. She points to an engagement ring in the window. It had a diamond in it the size of a dacent turnip. 'This is the ring I have chose for my betrothal', says she and lugs me into the shop. So, seein' I was in the place anyway, I asked the boy behind the counter how much he was lukkin' fer the ring."

Robert John stopped in his narration. His hand shook visibly as he raised the mug to his lips and took a long draught of the whisky. It was obvious to Mick the postman was trying to fortify himself for what was coming next. The old farmer forgot about his own Cream of the Barley and waited patiently for Robert John to continue.

Robert John removed his Post Office issue peaked cap and flung it to the floor. "Mick," he snorted, giving his knee a hearty slap with the palm of his hand to give added emphasis to his next words, "Mick, as true as I'm sittin' on this sate, the money that boy wanted for thon ring wud have bought me a good farm of land! 'Oh, that ring is the desire of my heart' declared Martha Kate as she noted the blood drainin' from my face. 'I cannot live without it,' says she."

Robert John took another gulp from his mug and smacked his lips. "Ye'll live with less, Martha Kate, says I as I wheeled her out through the door and marched her up to the bus-stop that quick her feet niver got a chance to hit the ground. She niver spoke a word the whole way out to the Cottown. I was livin' at the Cottown in them days. But as she gets off the bus at the stop before mine, she declares for the entire bus to hear that she will give me one whole day to come to my senses an' make an honest wumman of her!"

"A tartar," commiserated Mick, raising his glass, taking a sip and nodding knowingly.

"Tartar!" exclaimed Robert John, whose visage had now taken on the same warm glow as the brightly burning turf fire. "Tartar is bein' kind to her!" He held out his mug, his hand trembling. "Cud ye – wud ye have a wee drop more of the stuff ye have in that bottle, Mick?"

Mick looked doubtfully at the full-time postman, part-time farmer. "Do you not think you've had enough, Robert John? What about Lizzie Reid's hill?"

"Niver – niver you mind about Lizzie Reid's terrible hill," slurred Robert John. "I will surmount it. On my … on my knees, if necessary!" He held out the mug and again placed no restriction upon his host as he poured out the liquid.

"Thank ye, Mick. And a merry … a merry Christmas 'til ye – which is more than I iver had!" Robert John knocked back a volume of whisky, which didn't get a chance to excite his taste buds before it hit his stomach and further lit up his senses. "Anyway. As I was sayin'. It crossed my mind I might have a bit of thinkin' to do about this whole shebang. So I did. I tuk myself off into the fields on Christmas mornin' an' thought the whole thing out. Robert John, says I to meself. Ye're a fool. Here you are, not even married, an' this wumman has ye underneath her thumb. Are ye a man or a mouse? Get up an' face her with it man. Tell her straight to her face she'll have to change her way of goin' if she wishes to spend any more time in your company."

Robert John fortified himself with another drop of liquor and wiped his mouth. "So I did. I went straight over the fields to her da's farm. I was clean mad. Anyway, when she came to the door I informed her she was nothin' but a – nothin' but a – a money-grabbin' hussy, an' from now on, if she wanted to marry me, I

⎯⎯ ⚭ ⎯⎯

wud control the purse strings, an' I wud be the boss – the way a man should be!"

"You could do nothin' less," agreed Mick, taking the opportunity to sup from his own tumbler. "And what did she say to that?"

"What did she say!" reiterated Robert John. "'Oh, says she, I would not care to give my hand in matrimony to you, Robert John Henry, not if you were the last man livin' in the whole of the Cottown and Ballyfotherley and Ballyhay as well! An' then if she didn't draw off an' hit me such a skelp across the jaw I wasn't able to shave for a week!'"

Mick laughed heartily and Robert John afforded himself a giggle as he took another draught from his mug. The postman wiped his mouth. "Well, Martha Kate," says I, "if that's not the best bit of news I heard since the day you fell into Andy Pollock's sheaugh and were hauled out clabber to the oxters, I do not know what is! An' I left her standin' there, in her own stack yard, her tongue failin' to engage in gear for the first time in recorded history." Robert John wiped his brow again. "It was a close call, Mick. A very close call. But it was a lesson learned. Ever since that I have tuk good care to stay well away from the weemin – an' weddin's of any sort. No matter who they belonged to!"

"You did well to get shot of that one," laughed Mick. "And what about her? Did she ever marry?"

"Never did," snorted Robert John. "She's livin' in misery yet. She put it around the entire countryside she had no need of Robert John Henry. She cud have any man she pleased. Her great problem was, she niver pleased any."

Robert John reached to the floor. After a few unsuccessful attempts he managed to pick up his Post Office issue peaked cap. He slapped it on his head at a ridiculous angle. "I'll … I'll have to be … I'll have to go, Mick. But ye … ye can understand why Christmas is not a particularly happy time for me. Too many painful memories. But thanks for the … thanks for the buttermilk, Mick. An'…an' the wee drop of whatever was in that bottle.

An' the wee bit of Christmas crack. An' now … now for Lizzie Reid's terrible hill!"

Mick looked on in genuine concern as Robert John rose somewhat shakily to his feet and took a few circuitous steps in the general direction of the front door.

"Robert John!" called Mick, rising to his feet and guiding the postman across the room. He pulled the door open for the postman. "Robert John! Maybe you should forget about Lizzie's hill. You're in no fit state to climb it. Not in this snow!"

Robert John shook himself free from his host's restraining arm. He staggered toward the big red bicycle. "Do not … do not worry 'bout me, Michael. His Majesty's mails must get … they must get through! And I am entrusted to see they do!"

Mick shook his head as Robert John somehow threw his leg over his big red bicycle and wobbled down the lonen to make the initial approach for the assault on Lizzie Reid's terrible hill.

Robert John Henry, full-time postman, part-time farmer, never made it up Lizzie Reid's terrible hill. Not even half way up. He was discovered lying upended in a snow-filled ditch two hours later by the driver of Inglis's bread-cart. The bicycle lay on top of the postman, his bag of letters and Christmas cards scattered all over the snow. Robert John was unhurt, but clearly not in his right senses. He made no attempt to rise from where he had fallen, but periodically broke into song extolling the virtues of whisky and wild, wild women, interspersed with complaints about the terrible price of engagement rings and the steepness of Lizzie Reid's terrible hill.

Half the countryside was rounded up to get Robert John on to his feet and his letters gathered together. When the cause of the postman's misadventure was established it was universally agreed it would be totally impossible for Robert John to make another attempt on Lizzie Reid's hill, or finish the rest of his run. The remainder of His Majesty's Royal Mail was delivered, courtesy of Inglis's bread-cart and its driver. Robert John was also delivered, courtesy of Inglis's bread-cart and its driver, to a neighbouring farmhouse where he was sobered up with copious mugs of black tea and, at his own request, two good mugs of buttermilk, after which he fell asleep for the best part of an hour. When he woke he was declared fit to throw his leg over the big bicycle. He was pointed in the general direction of Donaghadee where he arrived at the former Bridewell under his own steam and in good time to sign off for the day. The scandalous affair was hushed up. Although every duck and banty and Rhode Island Red about the countryside knew of Robert John's misadventure, not a word of it ever reached the Head Postmaster. Robert John's forty-five year good conduct record remained intact and unsoiled.

But the whole business severely shook Robert John. He decided he'd had enough of Lizzie Reid's terrible hill. He took early retirement, complete with full honours and a gold watch. In later days he often called in with Mick and always at Christmas time. He'd talk and yarn about the old days and always insisted Bing Crosby's great success with *White Christmas* was a flash in the pan and wouldn't last. Occasionally he'd slake his thirst with a good mug of buttermilk. But never again did he ever let Mick talk him into partaking of a little Cream of the Barley when he called in with the old farmer, to enjoy a wee bit of Christmas crack.

A Mysterious Meeting

A very strange thing happened to me the last time I visited The Upstart Crow. Many years after the events of that night I am still no nearer an understanding of them, much less making an attempt to explain them. I merely set down here, without comment, what happened on that evening. The reader must draw his or her own conclusion of what I saw and heard.

Although the strange circumstances in which I found myself did not take place in my beloved Ards, but on the other side of the world, they did happen to me, a man of the Ards. As a storyteller and writer it would be a simple task for me to change the setting of the unusual events of that night and portray them as happening close to the place I call home. But I prefer to be true to my reader. I believe the experience of what befell an Ards man, myself, so far away on that night, is worthy to be noted in the pages of this volume with all the factual details remaining intact.

The Upstart Crow, for those of you who have never had the pleasure of entering its portals, is a coffeehouse and bookstore. It describes itself as the book-lover's companion and coffee-lover's best friend, sentiments that I can wholeheartedly endorse. I first chanced upon it when visiting some dear friends in California's beautiful old western town of San Diego, right on the coast of the blue and warm Pacific Ocean.

You'll find The Upstart Crow in the Seaport Village area of town, a lovely area by day and even more beautiful at dusk, an idyllic place to enjoy a balmy evening and experience spectacular sunsets as they splash the bay with daubs of gold right in front of you. When night settles in the Village takes on a strange mystical magic. Narrow twisting old-fashioned lamp-lit lanes lead you round and round past dozens of unusual little shops and eateries. It's a world away from the rush and hurry of modern life, a place where folk of all ages walk hand in hand and dream their dreams.

The Upstart Crow is indeed the book-lover's companion. It's a wooden building, made from old wood, wood you can smell and touch. You can feel it springing and creaking beneath your feet, lulling the senses with a feeling of old times, old strengths, old values. The counters are wooden, the stairs to the upper floors are wooden, the bookshelves, smoothed and worn by countless fingers which have run along them through the years, are wooden. The chairs and tables where book-lovers and coffee-lovers lounge and enjoy are wooden. A sense of peace, calm and tranquillity, and of always being here, wraps itself warmly around you. The smell of wood and of thousands of books, the best books, is everywhere, mingling with the delightful fragrance of freshly ground coffee-beans and the warm odour of coloured candles flickering in little ruby coloured bowls on the walls and tables.

This unusual tabernacle to the lovers of good books and good coffees is a maze of little departments, not laid out in any order, but each one leading you coyly into the next, then deeper and deeper into the intoxicating labyrinths of its interiors. On my first visit my curiosity led me on in many circles and wanderings. The strange thing was that when I retraced my steps to where I had begun my browsing I seemed to be in yet another area I had not previously encountered and I happily began to discover its delights all over again. When I finally tore myself away and paid for the pile of books nestling in my arms I asked the owner of the bookshop – an old man with shoulder length white hair, how the place came by its unusual name.

"Well," said Al, for that was the old man's name, "You probably know coffee-houses were popular gathering places for literary Londoners in 16th century England, and for many generations of writers after that. It's said a minor playwright by the name of Robert Greene was jealous of Shakespeare and indirectly accused him of stealing his material. Apparently he labelled the Bard "an upstart crow, beautified with our feathers, that with his tiger's heart wrapped in a player's hide, supposes he is as well able to bumbast out a blank verse as the best of you." Al smiled. "Well, I like to think I'm continuing the tradition of the old coffee-houses and the writers of bygone days and the original upstart crow who has inspired countless generations."

Al waved a hand at his crammed bookshelves. "Book-lovers, book-browsers and struggling authors frequent this place. They discuss books, or their own work and maybe perform snatches from it. They criticise and encourage each other. Some of them spend a whole night in here with their scribbles. They read my books. Mostly they never buy more than a cup of coffee!" Al grinned. "I don't mind. I'm a booklover myself. And I learned a long time ago there's more to life than money. I get by. But some-times I think there's a lot more going on in this place than we realise. I like to think the spirit of the great authors dwell within these walls… Hardy, Tolstoy, O Henry, Dickens – why, maybe even the Bard himself!"

If the strange happenings that befell me that night in The Upstart Crow well over a year later is any sort of measure, I don't believe Al was very far wide of the mark in his musings. I had just returned to town after a pleasant day with my friends up at Point Loma. My last book had been published a couple of months earlier. The folks in my hometown of Newtownards and round about seemed to have enjoyed it. But I was exhausted. I felt I had written myself out. So I decided to spend an hour or two in the old bookshop, hoping to find inspiration for a Christmas story I usually wrote every year for the *Newtownards Chronicle*. December was already here. I hadn't got a single word down on paper, nor even the ghost of an idea what my seasonal offering might be. But when the chips were down I found inspiration usually came when I locked myself away in a room full of books, letting my mind wander where it would, picking up a scrap here, a thought there, until I had many handfuls of such orphans as might warm my heart and present me with the first line of my story. That's all I would need. The first line….

I sat down in the wooden chair, my elbows on the wooden table, a cup of coffee and a copy of *The Mystery of Edwin Drood* for company. As usual, the place was well filled, browsers at the bookshelves and more serious types slumped in their chairs, oblivious to everything but the words and thoughts within the volumes into which they so intently peered. I drank cup after cup of coffee and lost myself in the unsolved mystery of Edwin Drood. I was thus engaged when I heard the voice.

"I do beg your pardon, sir. Please forgive my disturbing your thoughts, but the establishment is more than usually full this evening. Would it be a great inconvenience if I were to ask if I might partake of a seat at this table?"

The voice was not American: it was articulate, rich, the annunciation of each word perfection in itself. It was a commanding voice but not a demanding one, almost quaint in style, the voice of one who perhaps had spent some time upon the stage, delivering with ease and clarity words that were his stock in trade. I half glanced up, about to give the owner of the voice a token wave to take the other chair. But if the man's voice had made an instant impact upon me it was nothing to the impression its owner made upon my visual senses. The man, not overly tall, indeed slightly stooped and not young, leaned with one hand upon the empty chair. The angular face was that of a gentleman in perhaps his late fifties, with quick darting eyes that gleamed with light, a high forehead with a receding hairline but an abundance of greying brown hair that fell nearly to the shoulders of his long green velvet jacket. A heavy moustache hid his upper lip and continued round both sides of his mouth and down into a narrow beard several inches in length. A heavy gold watch-chain, which gleamed in the lamplight, curled its way into his waistcoat pocket. A bright emerald green silk cravat was at the man's throat, embellished with a bejewelled tie-pin set in a tiny house of gold. His waistcoat was the colour of corn and matched the tone of his check trousers.

A name for this person sprang immediately to my mind and almost to my lips. But the idea was ridiculous, impossible, and just in time I checked myself from uttering it aloud. I had seen many photographs very similar in appearance to this man. But they were always in black and white or faded sepia. I knew much about the man in those photographs. But this could not be the same person. It wasn't possible.

The man tilted his head. His lips broadened slightly in a little smile as he noted my hesitation. "I do inconvenience you sir," he said softly. "Please forgive me!"

"N-no," I mumbled as the gentleman made to move away. "Please. By all means, take the chair. I was adrift in another world. Your voice startled me."

The man thanked me as he pulled back the chair and made himself comfortable, immediately directing a question to me. "And, if I may be so bold to inquire sir, precisely which world were you in? Not the present, I presume? Over many years I have learned most of the personages who patronise this delightful establishment, and others like it, have a certain tendency to dwell, if not in, then at least upon, other times, and other places than where they actually are!"

I relaxed, warming to the figure before me. An actor. That's what he was. An actor. That would make sense. A strolling player.

Probably doing a reading here tonight. Actors, poets and writers – they were always doing that sort of thing at The Upstart Crow – impromptu, off the cuff – though this was the first time I'd ever seen one in costume at the bookshop.

"Well," I nodded, in partial agreement. "I must admit my thoughts were indeed of other times and other places. I'm a writer, of sorts. Nothing very serious. But sometimes I become so involved plotting a story in my head I loose track of what is going on around me. I dropped in here this evening in hope of finding some inspiration for a Christmas story. I enjoy Christmas. I like to write about it. But with every year that passes it becomes more and more difficult to find a new idea."

"Ah yes. Your Christmas stories," murmured my table companion. "Quite delightful. I have read them. Often you make mention of myself within their pages."

I blinked and stared hard at the stranger before me. "You – you have read my work! But that's not possible. And with respect, I do not think I mention you in any of my stories. This is the first time we have met."

The man stroked his small paddle-shaped beard. He smiled, evidently amused at my confusion. "Are you not an author, sir? And are not your writings available to the general public in return for a few coins of the realm?" Here the man stopped and covered a little cough with the palm of his hand. "But I must apologise. I have quite forgotten my manners." He stretched a white-cuffed arm across the table. "Dickens, sir. My name is Charles Dickens. Delighted to make your acquaintance!"

I was totally at a loss to know what was going on. That the man looked and dressed exactly like Charles Dickens and, for all I knew, probably spoke exactly like him, there wasn't the slightest doubt. The bright colours of the man's attire did surprise me. But then I'd always formed my impression of my favourite author only from such black and white and sepia photographs as existed. But that this player should introduce himself in character and not by his real name, whatever it was, surprised me. Still, this was

The Upstart Crow. Probably everybody who patrolled its laby-rinth of bookshelves and little rooms were just a tiny bit off the beam from your average everyday citizen. I'd done a bit of acting myself. I knew enough to understand that if you wanted to be good you had to become, totally, the character you represented yourself to be. Just like this person at the other side of the table. So I joined in.

"I am very pleased to meet you, Mr Dickens," I smiled, return-ing his solid grip and firm handshake. "This is indeed a great honour. But I must confess I would not have expected to see you on this side of the American continent."

Mr Dickens waved a dismissive hand. "Time and distance are no longer of any consequence to me. I go where and when I please. Most often I return to the narrow streets and alleyways of old London Town. That is where my heart is. And of course to the leafy green lanes of Kent and my beloved Gads Hill."

I raised an eyebrow. This player knew his stuff. "I've visited your old home at Gads Hill," I said. "And Rochester. And Chatham. Often. I believe they still hold much of the charm they had in the days of *The Pickwick Papers.*"

"Indeed they do," agreed Mr Dickens. "And I have seen you there on occasions. Many times I have noticed you, in summer, walking through the fields and cherry orchards, past the little church where my dear daughter was wed."

I was stunned. The man was absolutely correct. Frequently, when staying with family friends, John and Margaret Hutchinson, in the village of Lower Higham, just down the road from Dickens former home at Gads Hill, I had indeed often strolled through the fields and past St. Mary's, the quaint little church where one of Dickens daughters had married. And as I ambled along I was very much aware the great writer had once upon a time walked the very pathway I now trod. But the tiny church and the long and isolated track that led to it were quite removed from the gen-eral life of the village. How did this man know of it? Much more surprisingly, how did he know it was a favourite haunt of mine? And that I had visited it on more than one occasion?

"You display a degree of surprise," said Mr Dickens, noting the shock clearly evident upon my face. "Pray, why is this? In one of your own stories do you not quote the words 'there are more things in heaven and earth than are dreamt of in our philosophy.' Why then your dismay?"

I tried to appear composed. But it was one thing to quote words in a work of fiction. It was quite another to have them acted out in front of you over a coffee table in one of America's great cities. But Mr Dickens rescued me from my dilemma by changing the subject. He tapped a forefinger on the volume lying before him. "*The Mystery of Edwin Drood*," he mused. "As you know, I never saw it published. You have read it?"

I shook my head. "No, Mr Dickens. I have not, though I sometimes browse through it. There is little of your work I have not enjoyed, but I have never seriously taken up Edwin Drood. You were not granted time to finish it. I do not see the point in reading a half completed book. I know one or two have attempted to finish the work after your – after your – when you left it, and claim to have done so in the manner and conclusion you yourself would have chosen. But I don't believe it is possible to justify such a claim."

Mr Dickens smiled. "Indeed. Who can truly know the mind of an author and his characters but the author himself? As you very well understand, my dear friend, we are simply vehicles who hold the pen and make the marks upon the page. Our characters, if they are to mean anything, and are true at all, must have a life and a mind of their own. They will come and go and do and say what they will, usually in a manner quite foreign to that which we have in mind for them. That indeed is part of the joy of authorship – we see characters and events and are privy to conversations no one has ever seen or heard before. It is our simple task and joy to listen, watch and set down what we see and hear – chiefly for our own edification. If we are fortunate, those who read our words may also receive some pleasure from our little offerings. Would you agree?"

"I would, Mr Dickens," I said wholeheartedly, "Though I certainly could not have expressed it half so well. Sometimes I listen for the voices and watch for the characters, and they are not there. But I never lift my pen and force them to come to me and do my bidding. I did, once. It was a disaster. The characters were neither genuine nor warm, the conversations and happenings contrived and worthless. I never attempted it again. So, I must wait – shall we say – until the real thing comes along."

"Well said sir," replied Mr Dickens, "and I would hazard a guess that thus far your waiting has never been in vain and always well rewarded." He spread his smooth white hands in an open gesture on the table. "Please forgive my boldness – but if I were to relate to you an idea I myself once had for a little Christmas story, would it be of some help to you?"

I smiled and shook my head. "You are very kind. But you know I could not take your material. The story is yours, peculiar to yourself."

Mr Dickens nodded. His eyes studied mine in the flickering candlelight. I knew he was assessing me and weighing my answer. "But my story was never published – indeed, not even committed to paper. Not so much as a scrap of it was ever laid down in my notebooks. But it had been in my mind and in my heart for a long time, even while I toiled with Drood. It would have been a simple little tale, but one I should dearly loved to have written."

Mr Dickens pulled a silk handkerchief from his pocket. He blew his nose and dabbed at a tear which began to roll down his finely featured face. "I do wish I had attempted it before Drood. I really do." Mr Dickens sniffed and carefully pushed his handkerchief back into a pocket. "Forgive me sir," he apologised as he composed himself. "How silly of me. But writing and the telling of tales was my life. My whole being. I do miss it. Terribly. Nothing – nothing can possibly compensate for the loss of it. But I wonder, would you be so kind – could you possibly – what

I mean to say sir is, would you at least avail me of a few moments of your precious time that I might relate to you the bare bones – the merest outline – of my little story? And if perhaps, in a time yet to come, you saw some appeal, a speck of worth within it – why sir, I should be delighted if you would set to work upon it and gave it sinew and muscle and the breath of life and perhaps publish that it may possibly bring pleasure to those who might take it up? Would you be so kind, sir? Even to listen?"

I looked at Mr Dickens, staring so earnestly and imploringly at me. I looked around the interior of The Upstart Crow and my fellow booklovers and connoisseurs of good coffees. Each person was immersed in his own particular passion. Not one gave so much as a glance at me or the table at which I sat, or to the strange and definitely eccentric gentleman who shared it with me.

My mind wandered back to something I had learned early in my writing career, something that had always stood me in good stead. Never, ever, refuse a commission of any sort, nor any invitation that may be extended to you, no matter how inadequate you may feel to accept the invitation or the challenge. You never knew where, by passing through a door that had been slightly opened for you, that door might lead, and what possibilities might lie beyond it. And here was Mr Charles Dickens, one of the greatest writers in the English language, inviting me, right here in The Upstart Crow, in Seaport Village in San Diego, to listen to his little tale. I smiled. It would be ungracious of me to decline his request. And this was certainly one opportunity which most definitely would not come my way again.

"Mr Dickens," I said, now throwing myself wholeheartedly headlong into the affair. "I am deeply honoured. It will be a great privilege for me to listen. Please. When you are ready. Begin your story.

The Christmas Story

I made myself comfortable in my chair and gazed across the table at Mr Charles Dickens. Suddenly it seemed the most natural thing in the world that the great author should be sitting opposite me in the old San Diego bookshop come coffee-shop so quaintly named The Upstart Crow. The book-lined walls housing the works of Tolstoy, Homer, Hardy, Shakespeare, and Mr Dickens himself, to name but a few, was the perfect and most natural of environments to be in discussion with my favourite writer. I no longer questioned how it was possible he could be here in conversation with a Newtownards man well over one hundred years after he had written his last words. I could hardly wait for the great man to begin the tale he so wanted to tell.

I swear twenty years of time and age fell from Mr Dickens's face as he slipped easily into his discourse. His whole being surged with energy and fervour. His eyes gleamed with light and enthusiasm.

"My story, or should I say the bones of it, begins in old London town," began Mr Dickens, "in the wretched hovel of an aged personage to whom Providence has granted more years than any man has right to expect, but nothing in the way of health or worldly goods for his comfort in them. It is Christmas morning. The old man's teeth chatter with cold as he drags himself from his cot and wipes the back of a bony hand across the room's tiny frost-rimmed window. What little warmth there is in his hand is not sufficient to make an impression upon the veneer of ice upon the glass but he peers, it seems with great eagerness and anticipation, through the frosted pane. Seeing nothing, he clutches his night-garment around him and hastens to the door. With great difficulty he draws the iron bolt which secures his pathetic dwelling and pulls the door open. He gasps as an icy wind stabs his chest and a flurry of wet snow lashes his thin face. He looks up the street, eyes searching. Then down the street. There is no one there, save the hot-chestnut seller blowing into his freezing hands as he contemplates his smoking brazier, which stubbornly refuses to light. At the other end of the snowy thoroughfare a baker's boy, flushed with the enthusiasm of life as only a baker's boy can, whistles cheerfully as he stumbles through the snow with a tray of steaming bread upon his head. The old man sighs, steps back into his humble abode, and forces the door closed behind him. He does not secure the bolt.

The old man has neither kith nor kin. Neither does he enjoy the luxury very few of us enjoy, if we had but the wisdom to acknowledge it, that of a true friend. His peers and companions have long since departed this scene. For many years he has lived as one alone, a stranger in a strange place, one who has outgrown his time. But today, despite the cold in the hearth and the chill in his bones, there is a spring in the old man's step and a song within his heart. This day, this very Christmas Day, the old man expects a visitor. A friend, a true friend, who will, without fail, call upon him.

In the dark shadows of the night just gone, Christmas Eve night, the old man dreamed a dream - a dream so striking and vivid in content and detail he knew for certain it was much more than just the night-time wanderings of his mind. In the stillness of the dark night the old man had a vision - a revelation of his Lord. And his Lord had given the old man the promise he would visit with him on Christmas Day. Now that precious day was here, he must prepare for his guest who might arrive at any moment.

The old man discarded his nightclothes and struggled into a bundle of rags, which might afford some degree of warmth for his feeble body. He sat down at the cold grey ashes of yesterday's meagre fire and poked about them, collecting up in his freezing fingers those few pieces of cinders which had not fully burned away and might be of value to commence a new blaze to warm his coming visitor.

The grate was cold. The ashes and what pieces of fuel were left to him were of poor quality. A wet snow and a whistling wind howled down the chimney defeating all his attempts to ignite any sort of fire. The poor man fell to his knees the better to light the tinder and he was on his knees when the knock came to the door. Startled, he glanced up, shameful he did not at least have a cheerful and warming blaze for his guest who was already here. He rose from his knees and shuffled quickly to welcome his visitor.

But when he drew open the door the form standing before him was not the one he expected. It was nothing more than a small ragged boy, cheeks red as ruby apples and the hands he wrung together pinched blue with cold.

"Please sir," exclaimed the boy with an earnest fervour and a pleading in the bright eyes which immediately melted the old man's heart. "Please sir – if you please sir – could you spare some twigs – anything – with which I might light a little fire to warm my mother. She is with child soon to be born, perhaps even on this Christmas Day. She is alone sir, with no one to care, and it is cold. So cold. If you could sir – please…" Here the child left off from his pleading and buried his face in his hands.

The old man held up a bony arm. "Enough, my child! Speak

no more! Come!" And he ushered the fatherless child into his humble dwelling and burdened him down with such few sticks and pieces of fuel and tinder as lay in his own grate until nothing remained for his own fire and he knew that neither he nor the guest he expected would enjoy the blaze of a Christmas hearth on this blessed day.

The poor child had no sooner departed on his way rejoicing in his good fortune than the old man commenced to brush and tidy the lifeless hearth. Despite the pitiful condition in which he himself dwelled the old man was filled with an energy and strength he had not known for many years. He swept every corner of the room, polished the little window-pane through which the cold red sun now shone, made his bed and only then did he lay his table with the best of the meagre fare within his cupboard. He was sorrowful there would be no welcoming fire for his coming visitor. But upon his table there would be hospitality, slight though it may be. He laid two plates and two jugs on the rough table and in the centre of it the remnants of a mouldy cheese. A half loaf of bread was placed beside the cheese with a little drink and the old man had only just set down the remains of his pickle jar when a knock fell upon his door. The old man smiled. His visitor was come.

But his visitor was not come. It was indeed a man who stood in the doorway, a man as aged and stooped and surely as poor as himself, indeed, even more so. The figure, dressed in nothing more than a snow-covered bundle of rags tied about his wasted body with a piece of rough twine, raised a feeble hand to the old man's face.

"Bread, kind sir! Bread! A morsel only, for pity's sake, that my body which has not known nourishment for many days might even now be strengthened!"

The old man stared in dismay at the stranger on his doorstep. The man's face was shockingly thin and pale and the eyes so sunken and lifeless in their sockets he was more of an apparition than one who had muscle and bone and flesh and blood. He grasped the figure's hand, deathly cold, and led him back into his chamber, giving a silent prayer of thanks that his own situation was so much more comfortable than that of many others on this Christmas Day.

The old man led the stranger to his table. Gently he set him down and bade him eat as he would and did not himself partake of any thing that was upon the table. The beggar gratefully feasted upon the mouldy cheese and hard bread and dry pickle, a feast such as he had not known for many a day, a feast which did indeed give him a little succour and strength before he set out again, an ancient desolate relic, to wander the streets of nothingness on his journey to nowhere.

The old man shook his head and closed his door and set about clearing his table, which now held not enough food to interest even a mouse. He thought of his coming visitor. It grieved him sorely he was left with neither warmth nor food to offer his guest. He fretted and dusted and cleaned, all the while thinking of the great shame that would be his when his beloved guest arrived and found him entirely without means of entertaining him. He was thus anxiously employed when a third knock came to his door. With trembling hand the old man laid down his dirty rag and broom and composed himself to finally greet the one he had waited for all the day.

But still his wait was not ended. Before him stood a young girl of tender years, a waif, a desolate soul who would have been nothing less than beautiful had her circumstances been any other than those she had undoubtedly been born into. Her gentle blue eyes rested on the old man's and despite her great need he could see the dignity, yet tenderness, within them.

"Matches, sir. Please – please will you buy my matches? To light your Christmas fire, and perhaps a Christmas candle in memory of the dear One who gave us this blessed day?"

The old man shook his head in shame and sorrow and guilt and compassion as the little girl offered him a tiny box from beneath her thin shawl, which clung wetly to her slender frame. "My little one," he sobbed, in great distress, "I have nought to offer you! Not even a penny, nor yet a piece of bread to give you strength for the day. Alas, my house is empty!" The old man hesitated. Suddenly a smile wreathed his worn and weary countenance and his eyes brightened. "But! Hold, dear child! Once I had a little grand-daughter. She dwelled with me here until that day she was called away to her heavenly home. Within my humble abode I have retained her little clothes, being all of her I have yet remaining to me. You may have them, dear child, with her blessing and with mine, and perchance they will serve you better than the pitiful threads which do you no service on such a day as this!"

And the little waif departed from the old man and went on her way, so rejoicing in her new found warmth and comfort she hardly felt the pains of hunger that ravished her little body.

Once more the old man shuffled into his barren room and in exhaustion threw himself into his chair. What delayed his special guest, the one he had expected from the first light of this morning? So many others, knocking upon his door, but never the one he looked for. Why did he not come as he had promised? Now Christmas Day was more than half spent.

And the minutes ticked on and on and the clocks of old London town struck the hours one after the other and yet there came no knock upon the door. Then the darkness fell and it was night, cold, bitter night, and the candle, such as it was, would soon give out, and although he could not understand the reason, the old man knew his guest would not come now.

The clocks of old London town had long since struck eleven of the hour when the old man at last lifted the now feebly flickering candle and turned into his bed. He propped his head against the hard bolster and wearily picked up his book, his precious book, from the little table on which he had set his candle. His spirit was low within him and he was saddened beyond measure, unable to understand why his Lord had not come to him as he had promised. With a heavy sigh, the sigh of one for whom life holds no remaining happiness or joy, he opened his book. Immediately his eyes fell upon the words:

'I was an hungered, and ye gave me meat; I was thirsty and ye gave me drink; I was a stranger and ye took me in; naked, and ye clothed me… inasmuch as ye have done it unto one of the least of these my brethren, ye have done it unto me…'

The book slipped from the old man's hand. A little smile came upon his visage and his eyes shone and his soul filled with a deep, deep peace and contentment, such as he had never known. He knew he was blessed beyond measure. His Lord had called upon him, not once, but three times. The old man's aged lips gave forth a prayer of gratefulness and thanksgiving and understanding as his candle finally flared up into a great light which flooded the whole chamber, then faded, and gave light no more.

As the clocks of old London town pealed out the closing of the last hour of Christmas Day, the One the old man had waited for with great diligence came to him once again, closed his eyes and carried him away on his breast to that place where there is no more hunger or sorrow or pain or want, to the place eye hath not seen, nor ear heard, the things which God hath prepared for them that love him."

Mr Dickens finished his story and I hardly knew what to say or where to look as he sighed and again dabbed at his eyes. He was quite exhausted, drained in the telling of his tale. I gave him time to regain his composure. Then I broke the silence.

"Mr Dickens," I murmured, "this would indeed have been a beautiful story. I very much regret you never had the opportunity to write it. But I thank you for sharing even the bare outline of it with me." I pushed away my cold coffee cup. "But I am forgetting my manners! This place is famous for more than just excellent books and great coffees! To celebrate our meeting, will you join me in a pot of good English tea before we close our evening?"

Mr Dickens smiled and gave a little bow with his head. "Gladly. I am most grateful."

I made my way to the counter where the teas and coffees were served and asked Al for a pot of his finest tea and two cups. Al smiled.

"Two cups? Who's the other one for?"

I pointed across the bookshop. "Why, for my friend Mr Dickens, of course."

"Sir," replied Al. "What friend? There's no one there. Matter of fact, there isn't anyone anywhere. You and I are the only two left in the whole place. Everyone has long since gone. It's a quarter after midnight. I wait for you and then I close. Sure has been a long day."

I stared around the bookshop. Al was right. It was empty. Deserted. I turned my head to the table where I had listened so attentively to Mr Dickens tell his story of a Christmas of long ago. He wasn't there.

"But – but the gentleman I have been with all evening – Mr Dickens – he was there – at my table – just a moment ago! He's only just finished telling me one of his Christmas stories!"

Al shook his head as he began to extinguish the candles and turn off the lights.

"My friend, you've been sitting at that table, quite alone, all evening. Staring into empty space for most of it." He shrugged. "I've seen it happen before in The Upstart Crow. Not often. Maybe a couple of times. Two winters ago it was Tolstoy. Young feller swore he'd been talking to him all evening, garnering help for the Great Russian novel he was going to write. Funny thing is, the kid wrote it. Published it too. Darndest thing!" Al pointed across the shop to a row of bookcases against the back wall. "It's right over there. Never travelled farther than Orange County in his entire life – sits down and writes a thousand pager set in Russia in the last century. Good book. Sells well. Sure beats me how he did it." He shrugged again. "Maybe there is something going on in this place – the thoughts and words of so many great writers contained within these walls. The new thoughts and new words, of so many others who come here, almost to worship – something's got to rub off somewhere. Maybe the past and the present and the future and the real and the unreal, and what we know and what we think we know and what we don't know – maybe they become a sort of melting pot that has to give birth to something. But then, what do I know? I'm just a bookseller. I can't explain it."

I couldn't explain it either. Then or now. But The Upstart Crow is more than just a bookshop. I'm convinced of it. There is something going on there. If you ever find your way to old California, and San Diego and Seaport Village, make sure you pay a visit to The Upstart Crow. It'll be an experience you'll never forget. Now, I'm not saying you'll encounter Hardy or Homer, or Dickens or Tolstoy, or even the Bard, the original upstart crow. But then again, you never know. You just never know…

Happy Christmas!

Dear Reader

I hope you have enjoyed this publication from Ballyhay Books. It is one of a growing number of local interest books published under this imprint including Hugh Robinson's books *Back Across the Fields of Yesterday* and *The Book of One Thousand Beautiful Things and Other Favourites*, John O'Sullivan's *Belfast City Hospital, a Photographic History*, Viv Gotto's *Footprints in the Sea* and *Lie Over Da* by Aideen D'Arcy.

To see details of these books as well as the beautifully illustrated books of our sister imprint, Cottage Publications, why not visit our website at **www.cottage-publications.com** or contact us at:–

Laurel Cottage
15 Ballyhay Rd
Donaghadee
Co. Down
N. Ireland
BT21 0NG

Tel: +44 (0)28 9188 8033

Timothy & Johnston

BALLYHAY BOOKS